THE
QUEST

THE
QUEST

THE
QUEST

EXPLORING CREATION'S HARDEST PROBLEMS

TODD CHARLES WOOD

NASHVILLE, TENNESSEE

Todd Charles Wood is president of Core Academy of Science.

Published by
New Creation, Nashville, TN 37204

First printing 2018

Printed in the United States of America

Wood, Todd Charles
The Quest: Exploring Creation's Hardest Problems
Includes bibliographical references and index.

CONTENTS

PROLOGUE

This is my story. I am a scientist and a Christian and a young-age creationist. I am driven by curiosity about God's works. I wonder about the stars and planets, the mountains and valleys, and the plants and animals that God made. I wonder how they came to be the way they are. I wonder *why* they came to be the way they are. I've spent most of my life studying God's creation and trying to understand it better.

I grew up in a Christian home, and I've been a creationist as long as I can remember. I went to Christian schools from Kindergarten through my college graduation. I even thought about studying theology in graduate school, but science was always my passion. In my graduate work, I studied evolution—not just "microevolution" but the full-blown macroevolution of all organisms. Because I was so interested in the origin of life and the diversity of species, I felt like I needed to really understand evolution. Using computer tools and protein sequences, I studied the purported evolution of the cells from which everything else supposedly evolved. After graduate school, I spent some time working on the rice genome project, and then I joined the Center for Origins Research at Bryan College, where I would develop much of my understanding of creationist biology and especially created kinds.

My background, with its amalgamation of creation studies and evolutionary biology, makes some people extremely uncomfortable.

If you listen to my critics, I'm supposed to suffer from something called "cognitive dissonance," which according to Wikipedia is a "mental discomfort (psychological stress) experienced by a person who simultaneously holds two or more contradictory beliefs." Because I can (and do) articulate and explain evolution like an actual evolutionist, creationists wonder how I can "believe" evolution and still be a creationist. For the same reason, evolutionists can't understand why I would still believe such "nonsense" about God and creation.

To be honest, until people pointed it out to me, I never knew that my way of thinking was so difficult. It just came naturally to me, and I never really thought about *how* I thought. I just did it. Over the past twenty years, I've interacted with a lot of different people with a lot of different views about creation and evolution. I'm happy to report that I'm not the only one who thinks the way I do about these questions. I've discovered lots of like-minded creationists with a good understanding of evolution and a strong commitment to young-age creationism.

I've also discovered that most people are confused (and a little threatened) by the way I think and talk about creation and evolution. I've had to work hard to articulate not just what I think but the *way* I think. To be honest, *what* I think is always changing, mostly because I'm always learning. I could tell you a little about what I think (and I will), but how I got to that point is really more important.

The most important thing, though, is where I'm going next. I've come to see my life as a quest. Life is full of challenges and problems and hard questions. Most of the time, the answers aren't obvious. Occasionally we see glimpses of God's plan after the fact, but often we find ourselves called to trust him without knowing how things are going to turn out. I'm on a journey, but it's not just any journey. I know exactly where I'm going. I'm on my way to a better understanding of God's creation and ultimately God Himself. As I think about this search for understanding, I like to think of it as a quest. It's not simply a journey, where I have a map and know how to get to my goal. It's not an expedition either, where I'm just randomly exploring. "Quest" implies a goal without knowing exactly how to achieve it.

The following chapters will guide you as you explore the quest. We begin with the most basic conflict that every Christian faces: How do I reconcile God's Word with my own experiences? With this dilemma in mind, we will then look at different ways Christians respond and the advantages of the quest. I'll illustrate how the quest has functioned in my own research and how it has shaped my thinking. The final chapters will examine the moral dimensions of the quest and our life together as the body of Christ.

Throughout the book, we'll stop and examine parts of God's creation to remind ourselves of the awe and wonder of the Creator. These pauses come between the chapters, and I've labeled them *Adoremus*, Latin for "let us worship." The name is inspired by listening to "O Come All Ye Faithful" in Latin on my parents' old record player, where the chorus repeats the phrase *venite, adoremus*, "come, let us worship." If you'd prefer to follow the flow of the book, you could skip these worship interludes. If you do, I hope you return and read them once you've finished the chapters. Because if you only approach the quest as a puzzle to solve or a problem to be worked out, you've really missed the point. The quest begins with curiosity inspired by the amazing and beautiful things that God made. We should all stop and remind ourselves regularly of the power and majesty and glory of the Creator we pursue. He alone makes this quest worthwhile.

So this is my quest. My goal is understanding God and his creation. I'll be on this quest my entire life. I probably won't reach my goal this side of the kingdom, but the quest brings me more joy and satisfaction than anything else I could spend my time on. As you read this book, I hope the quest will make sense to you. I hope you'll see how thrilling and wonderful the quest can be. Most importantly, I hope that you'll join me and experience the quest for yourself.

1
FAITH, SCIENCE, AND ACOSTA'S QUEST

Even though I'm a scientist by training, I have become more and more fascinated with the history of ideas over the past twenty years. I can't recall where my interest began, but I do remember spending a lot of time in graduate school tracking down the history of evolutionary thought in my own field of biochemistry. I would learn about evolutionary ideas in class or in my own research, and they were hard to explain from a creationist standpoint. I wanted to understand where those ideas came from. What were the main evidences? How had they been interpreted by biochemists and biologists of the past? Could there be explanations other than evolution? This led me to the basement of the library.

The library basement held all the dusty, old resources that were not in high demand. Current books and journals were on the main floor, and the basement was mostly occupied by students trying to study. It was pretty quiet down there. It seemed like I was the only student down there actually using the collections rather than the study carrels. Digging up that history gave me a bigger perspective on evolutionary biochemistry than I got in my research or in the classroom. History taught me that I wasn't alone in my questions. I discovered individuals like me, trying to make sense of their faith and the world around them. Some of them even had some pretty good ideas that had unfortunately been long forgotten. You never know what you might find in an old, dusty book.

After I finished my Ph.D., I continued to study the history of ideas every chance I got. I collected old creationist books and magazine articles, and I started reading even older stuff. First, I studied Darwin's life and history. That led me to explore the evolutionary thinking that preceded him. That led me to the design arguments of William Paley and John Ray. That led me to the scientific revolution itself and the famous trial of Galileo.

Somewhere in the midst of all this, I stumbled across José de Acosta. Acosta was a Catholic missionary who spent about fifteen years exploring and evangelizing Peru in the late 1500s. I don't remember how I found him, but I really responded to the questions and issues that Acosta confronted in his writings.

We begin our quest here with Acosta's story.

Faith in a New World

Christian Europe experienced a series of huge upheavals during the 1500s. The century began shortly after Christopher Columbus initiated the age of exploration, and Europeans discovered that they hardly knew anything about the larger world. Martin Luther sparked the Protestant Reformation and challenged people to re-examine their beliefs about the Bible, theology, and the authority of the Catholic Church. In 1543, two books appeared that would start a revolution in the world of "natural philosophy," what we now call science. Copernicus' *On the Revolutions of the Heavenly Spheres*, the more famous of the two, suggested that the earth might actually orbit the sun, instead of the other way around. Vesalius' *On the Fabric of the Human Body* inspired doctors and their students to question ancient authorities and to check things out for themselves.

In the midst of these revolutions, Acosta began his work in Peru in 1572, when he was just 32 years old. In his homeland of Spain, Acosta learned the scholastic disciplines of philosophy and theology, but this learning sometimes clashed with what he himself experienced traveling around Central and South America. His 1590 book *Historia Natural y Moral de las Indias* described the many surprises he found in the "New World."[1]

Acosta's book opens by discussing the structure of the world, explaining that the "antipodes" (what we call the southern hemisphere) were not much different from Europe. Many years earlier, classical philosophers had wondered what the world was like on the opposite side. They had a very simple concept of what we think of as gravity. If things fall "down," then anything on the opposite side of the earth would just fall off, right? Acosta reported that this was not at all correct. Things south of the equator fell to the ground just like they do north of the equator. Other ancient authors believed that the equator was so hot that it was uninhabitable and impassable. Acosta reported that the equator was surprisingly mild!

Because he lived at the very beginning of the scientific revolution, Acosta wasn't burdened with the science vs. faith wars that would start just a few decades after he published his book. He could look at a whole world's worth of discoveries with fresh eyes. When he observed things that the ancients thought were impossible, he corrected them, but there were other ancient teachings that still framed his way of thinking. The Bible in particular created some hard boundaries beyond which he was not willing to speculate.

When he observed animals found only in Central or South America but not in other parts of the world, Acosta wondered how they got there. He entertained the idea that God might have created them there (which is the easiest "explanation" for anything: God just made it that way), but he didn't think that was right. Why?

> For if the Creator produced them there, we need not have recourse to Noah's Ark, nor was it necessary to save all the species of birds and animals at that time if they were going to be created again later.[2]

In other words, the story of Noah and the ark wouldn't make any sense if God intended to recreate animals after the flood. Why bother preserving animals and people in an elaborate wooden boat if God just re-created animals after the flood?[3]

This question of unique animals and birds in South America perplexed Acosta for a long time, by his own admission. He specifically mentioned the guanacos, an animal like a llama that is native to Peru, but he also said that he could list thousands of animals that were common in Peru but totally unknown anywhere else in the world. Where did these animals come from?

Acosta wrote that it might be possible to classify the animals of Peru in the same species as the animals of Europe, Asia, or Africa. He recognized that human beings were diverse, and maybe the animals of Peru were diverse versions of species that were already known. He didn't really like this idea though because the differences were so great. As he wrote, "...to try to reduce them to species known in Europe would be like calling an egg a chestnut."[4]

All of this reasoning left Acosta with a basic outline of natural history: The animals of South America descended from ancestors of the same kind that survived the flood on Noah's ark. Since the ark landed in the Middle East, that meant that the ancestors of the unique Peruvian animals must have traveled to Peru from the landing place of the ark. How was that possible? After all, Acosta knew exactly what kind of a voyage that was, having crossed the Atlantic on a sailing vessel himself. How could animals get to Peru?

Acosta considered three scenarios to explain the presence of animals in South America. First, he speculated that people might have brought them. For some animals, that made sense. It was easy to imagine early people traveling with their livestock, but why would anyone want to deliberately transport animals that would eat their livestock, like wolves? As Acosta wrote, "it is laughable even to imagine it."[5]

Another possibility was that animals crossed the ocean on their own power, by swimming or flying. Again, though, Acosta had made this crossing himself, and he knew swimming across the Atlantic wasn't realistic.

So if animals didn't swim to South America, and they weren't carried by people, how did they get there? Acosta concluded that they must have walked. This is what he is chiefly remembered for: Acosta is one of the earliest writers who predicted that there must have been a land connection between the old world of Eurasia and the new world of the Americas. He had no way of knowing at the time, but his conjecture has become the accepted model to explain how the Americas became populated, at least by people. People walked across the Bering Strait from Siberia to Alaska during a time of low sea levels when the current sea floor was dry land.

Science and Faith Then and Now

Well, that's all very interesting, you might be thinking, but what difference does it make to us? We're interested in genomes, radiometric dating, fossils, and big bangs. How is some missionary from four hundred years ago going to help us understand all this modern science?

Acosta attempted what scholars today call an "integration of science and faith," a way of putting together what he knew from his religion with what his own scientific investigations seemed to be telling him. Over the past century, especially as scientists have continued to challenge sacred beliefs, religion scholars have shown a great interest in figuring out the "correct" relationship between religion and science. The most influential work on religion and science in the past sixty years was Ian Barbour's 1966 book *Issues in Science and Religion.*[6]

Barbour grouped religious responses to science into four categories: conflict, independence, dialogue, and synthesis. In conflict, science and religion fight and maybe even reject the other. Barbour placed young-age creationists and scientific atheists in this category. Other religious scientists might decide to hold their beliefs and science separately, insisting that the two do not conflict or even overlap. They are independent of one another. Science talks about the mechanics and structure of creation, and religion gives us values, meaning, and ethics. When a person starts to think about the ways that science and religion speak differently about common subjects like creation, that person has begun a dialogue between science and religion. Barbour's notion of synthesis encompassed ideas like natural theology, where scientific discoveries become evidence of God's attributes, and other efforts to reconfigure religion to conform more closely to what science has discovered.

Acosta fits rather poorly in Barbour's famous scheme. He obviously doesn't think that the scientific discoveries that he himself observed somehow contradicted his faith. He didn't hold his religion and science independently, either, since he thought the origin of the American creatures must have an explanation that was consistent with what he learned from the Bible. He also wasn't engaging in a simple dialogue, at least not in Barbour's sense of comparing and contrasting what science and religion say about the same subject. Acosta might have created a kind of synthesis but a very different sort than what Barbour proposed where science does not yield to religion.

If we were to take Barbour's word for it, because Acosta was a kind of creationist, he was therefore engaging in a conflict between science and religion. If that seems odd to you, it should. Barbour also placed scientific atheists in the conflict category with creationists, which is an even odder fit. What do Ken Ham and Richard Dawkins have in common? Apparently, they're both engaging in a "conflict" of science and religion.

When I look at Acosta or even at my own intellectual life, I don't see a conflict. I see in Acosta a faithful person trying to make sense of his world. I see a person who spent time observing and studying the world around him. I see him willingly correcting past mistakes but cautious about jumping to conclusions. I see him carefully examining just a few pieces of a much larger puzzle, without declaring immediately what the larger puzzle looks like. Acosta is meticulous, cautious, and wise. Acosta does not fit Barbour's mold. Acosta was something else.

Navigating Crisis

Now it might be easy for us to look down on Acosta from our place of knowledge and privilege here in the twenty-first century. We already know more about the animals of the Americas than Acosta could have even imagined. Thinking that way, though, we forget how much of a shock the Americas would have been to a learned person of the 1500s. The "simple" world of Europe, Africa, and Asia all connected to the resting place of Noah's ark was easy to understand. Animals got off the boat and wandered wherever they needed to go. So did people. With the Americas, though, Europeans found two vast continents full of unique animals. How could this make sense if the story of the flood was actually true?

Acosta faced the perennial struggle for people of faith. On the one hand, he knew what the Word of God said. He understood his own personal faith. On the other hand, he had his experiences that were hard to reconcile with what his faith told him was true.

This crisis is far truer to my Christian experience than Barbour's scheme ever was. This isn't a fight between knowledge of science and experience of religion. It's a confusion between two witnesses that we think are reliable but don't seem to make sense.

For many, this crisis of knowledge leads to simplistic but false answers. Some conclude the Bible is just wrong and God is a fairy tale. They fall away from the faith. Others decide the problem lies with the science. If science makes us uncomfortable with what we learned in church, then clearly science must not be trusted. This is the easy way out: just pick a side. In a crude sense, this is Barbour's "conflict."

Acosta and many others like him have chosen a more difficult path. Rather than succumb to crisis, Acosta continued to study and learn about South America while also remaining faithful to God and what he revealed to us in the Bible. He didn't try to ignore the open questions even though he didn't have all the answers that he wanted. That is the quest: an openness to learning and studying while remaining committed to God and his Word. Instead of capitulating to the "wisdom" of the world or shutting yourself off from the world of science, the quest seeks the truth that makes sense of both science and faith. The quest is a fifth step between the nonthreatening simplicity of dialogue and the firm conclusion of synthesis. The quest is science in one hand and the Bible in the other, seeking to understand them both. The quest is "faith seeking understanding."[7]

The quest does not lead to the kind of satisfaction that the world tells us we need. We're constantly challenged to have all the answers to the mysteries of creation, but what if the true path is to walk with the discomfort of not having easy answers? What if, like Acosta, we need to spend many years thinking and wrestling with our experiences and the leading of the Holy Spirit? What if we're not called to know all the answers? What if we're just called to be faithful with what little we do know?

In reality, now that I've been walking my own quest for twenty years, I find it immensely satisfying in ways I don't think others really appreciate. Too many people on all sides want everything to make sense right now, but waiting on the Lord to guide and direct my understanding brings wonderful glimmers of hope and excitement just when I least expect it. More about that later in the book, though.

What I admire most about Acosta is his faithfulness. He's willing to challenge and question ancient opinion and interpretation based on his own experiences, but he's also loyal to hundreds of years of Christian tradition and interpretation. He's careful and hesitant about questioning his own faith, and he thought long and hard about the questions that puzzled him. As he stood on the frontier of an unfamiliar, "new" continent, he also stood on the verge of a vast revolution in human knowledge, even though he never knew it.

We're very much in the same boat, except that our new frontier is the world of science. Where Acosta could ride a horse over the next hill and look around to make new discoveries, we use our microscopes, computers, space probes, satellite imagery, and DNA sequencers. Just in my lifetime, I've seen astonishing discoveries that Acosta never could have imagined. When I was a child, I witnessed humanity's first detailed images of other planets as the Voyager and Viking probes explored our solar system. As an adult, I've seen dinosaurs with feathers and the smooth surface of Pluto. I've even seen my own DNA that I inherited from my Neandertal forefathers.[8]

What will we discover tomorrow?

See, that's the real question. It's easy for us to snicker at these individuals from the past. But their struggles are the same as ours, and so is their ignorance. Oh sure, we know a lot more about a lot of things now, and knowledge is more accessible than ever before. But I think these advantages just make us all arrogant, as we look down on those poor, benighted souls of yesteryear. We know so little, but we pretend like we have all the important answers. The things we know today may well be the poor, benighted ignorance of tomorrow.

In the next chapter I'm going to try to bring Acosta's dilemma of faith and science into the present. I want to explore the ancient Christian faith and the frontiers of modern science, and I want us to see how they clash. Like Acosta, then, I want to chart a way forward. It's not a way of answers, though. It's a way of questions. It's a lifetime of discipleship seeking God's truth.

ADOREMUS 1

Ever since Darwin, scientists and laypeople alike tend to look at nature as Tennyson described it in 1849, "red in tooth and claw." Especially during Shark Week. The full stanza from Tennyson's In Memoriam A.H.H. *emphasized a longstanding theological puzzle:*

Who trusted God was love indeed
And love Creation's final law
Tho' Nature, red in tooth and claw
With ravine, shriek'd against his creed.[9]

The contrast here, and the contrast that Darwin struggled to understand, pits the loving God of theology against what appears to be a cruel and heartless world. Looking at today's world of predators and prey, of disease and death, of suffering and decay, we might find it hard to see God's love and grace.

But it's still there, lurking, sometimes in surprising places.

The largest clams in the world grow in the shallow seas of the western Pacific and Indian oceans. Giant clams can grow to around four feet in colossal, toothy shells. These clams don't eat people though, regardless of what you might have seen on Looney Tunes. Giant clams, like all clams, eat by sucking water in, filtering out what food particles happen to be in the water, and then squirting the water back out again. Doesn't sound very appetizing, but it gets the job done.

The funny thing is that giant clams only get about a third of their food from filter feeding. The other two thirds comes from algae that live inside the giant clam's body. All the really big giant clams have green algae living in an elaborate tube system specially made to protect those algae. As a young clam grows, microscopic algae enter the clam through an opening in its stomach that leads to the algae tube system. Even though the algae can re-enter the clam's digestive system through that same opening, they are not digested by the clam.[10] Instead, algae in giant clams make sugar from sunlight and carbon dioxide, and the clam takes sugar directly from the algae. Without these algae living inside them, young clams cannot grow to enormous sizes. In return for food from the algae, the clam provides a protected environment for the algae to live.

As we look across the magnificence of God's creation, it's easy to stop and linger on the lurid parts, the parts that remind us of our fallen, sinful world. We must not let those things distract us from the overwhelming beauty of creatures living in a wonderful harmony together, mutually dependent on one another. God made us a part of a bigger creation, a community of living things, all working together for the benefit not only of themselves but also of others. Creation reflects our own community as the body of Christ, working in harmony for the glory of God.

Psalm 133
Behold, how good and pleasant it is
when brothers dwell in unity!
It is like the precious oil on the head,
running down on the beard,
on the beard of Aaron,
running down on the collar of his robes!
It is like the dew of Hermon,
which falls on the mountains of Zion!
For there the Lord has commanded the blessing,
life forevermore.

2
HARD SCIENCE

In the first few months of 2010, I was working on a research
paper describing the *baraminology* of humans. Baraminology is
the field of creation research that tries to identify created kinds.
I had been working on mathematical ways of examining species
for more than a decade at that point, and I applied the techniques
to creatures as diverse as insects, horses, and sunflowers. The fall
of 2009 was my first foray into humans, and the results turned out
pretty well. Nothing surprising or dangerous: humans were humans
and apes were apes. That's good news! So I finished up my paper and
sent it to *Answers Research Journal* for peer review and publication.
The reviews were mostly positive with a few suggested changes, so
I got to work on making what I thought would be minor tweaks to
the manuscript.

Then *Australopithecus sediba* was announced to the world the
week of April 9, 2010.[11] Lee Berger, a Georgia-born paleontologist
living in South Africa, had been investigating possible fossil
locations in a large region called the "Cradle of Humankind,"
when his son stumbled across the first signs of the *sediba* skeleton,
a collarbone sticking out of a rock. The discovery made the cover
of the journal *Science*, and it was all over the news. Lee Berger's
research team was pretty blunt about what they thought it meant,
too: *Australopithecus sediba* was the most similar ape-like creature
to human beings. In evolutionary language, *sediba* was a "stem

taxon" or a "transitional form." This was yet another link connecting human beings to their supposed animal ancestors.

Other creationists were quick to claim that *sediba* was just another ape masquerading as a human ancestor.[12] I was intrigued and excited by the whole thing and inserted *sediba* into my own baraminology analysis of humans. I have to admit that I freaked out a bit when I got the results. My new analysis still showed a good separation between humans and apes, but *sediba* wasn't on the ape side. My results showed that *sediba* was human.

Naturally, I did what any scientist would do when they get dubious results: I did it again. I tried a different set of species. I tried a different set of characteristics. I tried everything I could justify scientifically. Every time, I got the same answer: *sediba* groups with the humans. So I had to accept it. Based on the data that I had and the techniques I used, *Australopithecus sediba* was human.

Because so many other creationists had so quickly judged *sediba* as non-human, I knew this research was going to get me in trouble. So I decided to fully own it. I changed the title of my paper from a harmless little description of my research to something like "*Australopithecus sediba* is human!"[13] I thought I might as well let everyone know what they were about to read.

Naturally, the responses were loud and mostly negative. To be honest, they had good reason to suspect that *Australopithecus sediba* was not human. The skeleton of *sediba* was far more ape-like than any other fossil that creationists judged to be human, but my analysis only examined the skull rather than the full skeleton. Up to that point, most creationists relied on skeletons more than skulls to tell what was human and what wasn't. The skeletons were pretty clear, too. There was a mostly human type of skeleton, where the arms and legs and backbones look very much like modern humans. There was also an australopith skeleton, where the arms and rib cages were more like chimpanzee arms but the legs were sort of like ours. For creationists, it was easy to see the human type as actual humans and the australopith type as nonhuman animals. *Australopithecus sediba* looked like a human in the head but an australopith below the neck.

Here Come the Missing Links

That strange mix of ape and human characteristics was something that modern creationists had never anticipated. From the very beginning of the evolution war, when Darwin's *Origin of Species* was first published, his critics asserted that the links connecting humans to apes were entirely absent, along with many other links between all the major types of creatures. This constant drumbeat became a sort of creationist doctrine: The so-called "missing link" was, is, and always will be missing. There are no transitional forms between humans and animals.

And yet, here is *Australopithecus sediba*, a creature with exactly the mix of characteristics that we might expect from a "missing link." But remember: There are no missing links! Since *sediba* didn't have a human-like skeleton, it must be an ape. It could not possibly be something in between. My disagreement was bound to make creationists uncomfortable (and even angry). I basically broke rank, which gives the evolutionists opportunity to laugh at us. After all, if it was so easy to tell the difference between humans and apes, then why don't all creationists agree about *sediba*? That's one reason my judgment about *sediba* is such a sore spot for other creationists. It's not only about whether *sediba* is human. It's much more fundamental. Creationist disagreement over *sediba* hints that the entire premise of "no missing links" might actually be wrong.[14]

Let's think about that for a moment, and let's try to put aside all our biases as creationists (yes, I know that's impossible, but let's try). Before we can say that there are no missing links, shouldn't we have an idea of what a missing link might look like? If by "missing link," we mean that creature that was the actual ancestor of all humans and whose parents were apes, then how would we know it if we saw it? It's not like a genealogy study where we can trace family records and find grave markers. All we get from fossils are bone shapes and sizes and occasionally some DNA. We can tally up differences and similarities but that's really it.

Maybe what we need to do then is look at lists of characteristics that distinguish humans and apes (here I'll use the chimpanzee as my generic "ape"), and maybe then we can think about what an intermediate form *might* look like (instead of insisting that this or that fossil is or is not an ancestor).

Characteristic	Human	Ape
Feet	Big toe flexes only up and down	Big toe flexes side to side for grasping
Thigh bone (femur)	Thigh bone meets the knee at an angle to keep feet directly under the center of the body	Thigh bone is straight to keep feet separated for walking on all four limbs
Hip bone (pelvis)	Round like a bowl	Flat
Forearm	Distance from the elbow to the wrist is shorter than the distance from the shoulder to the elbow	Distance from the elbow to the wrist is as long as the distance from the shoulder to the elbow
Foramen magnum (the hole of the skull that connects the brain to the spinal cord)	Connects the head to the spine on the bottom of the skull	Connects the head to the spine at the back of the skull
Brain size	Large, about 1300 cubic centimeters	Small, about 400-500 cubic centimeters
Muzzle	No muzzle	Pronounced muzzle
Forehead	Large, flat, and vertical	Very little. Bone around the eye is thick (brow-ridge), but the forehead itself is mostly absent

So what do we find in the fossil record? Are there creatures that we might plausibly say either have a mixture of these characteristics or something in between? Here are a set of fossil forms and how they scored on our chart:

Characteristic	Human	Neandertal	Homo erectus	Australopithecus sediba	Lucy (Australopithecus afarensis)	Chimpanzee
Feet	Big toe flexes only up and down	Big toe flexes only up and down	?	?	Big toe flexes only up and down (based on footprints)	Big toe flexes side to side for grasping
Thigh bone	Thigh bone meets the knee at an angle	Thigh bone meets the knee at an angle	Thigh bone meets the knee at an angle	Thigh bone meets the knee at an angle	Thigh bone meets the knee at an angle	Thigh bone straight
Hip bone	Round	Round	Round	Round but flared	Round but flared	Flat
Forearm	Distance from the elbow to the wrist is shorter than the distance from the shoulder to the elbow	Distance from the elbow to the wrist is shorter than the distance from the shoulder to the elbow	Distance from the elbow to the wrist is shorter than the distance from the shoulder to the elbow	Distance from the elbow to the wrist is as long as the distance from the shoulder to the elbow	Distance from the elbow to the wrist is as long as the distance from the shoulder to the elbow	Distance from the elbow to the wrist is as long as the distance from the shoulder to the elbow
Foramen magnum	Bottom of skull	Bottom of skull	Bottom of skull	Bottom of skull	Bottom of skull	Back of skull
Brain size	1300 cc	1600 cc	850-1100 cc	420 cc	415 cc	400-500 cc
Muzzle	No muzzle	Muzzle	Muzzle	Muzzle	Muzzle	Muzzle
Forehead	Large, flat, vertical	Pronounced browridge, little forehead	Pronounced browridge, little forehead	Pronounced browridge, little forehead	Pronounced browridge, little forehead	Pronounced browridge, little forehead

Now we could argue about whether these set of characteristics should tell us anything about evolutionary ancestors. We could even say (as I have done elsewhere) that in spite of all these characteristics, we can still use mathematics to identify what is human and what is not.[15] But for now, I want to ponder this chart for a moment here, because this isn't something creationists expected.

Take Lucy (*Australopithecus afarensis*) for example. Lucy is a partial skeleton discovered in Ethiopia in 1974. Lucy has three features in common with modern human beings, the big toe, thigh bone, and foramen magnum, all three of which are consistent with walking around on two legs. Lucy walked upright, sort of like we do. On the other hand, Lucy has four other features in common with the modern chimpanzee, mostly in her head. She has a pronounced muzzle, a small brain, and a heavy browridge. The proportions of her arms are suitable for climbing trees. Is Lucy *the* "missing link," an ape ancestor of all modern human beings? I don't know. No one could possibly know that, and there's not really any way to test for it either. But Lucy does have characteristics of both modern humans and modern apes *in one body*. Lucy is an intermediate.

If you read early creationist literature, they make it pretty clear that nothing will ever be found that bridges the gap between human and non-human. I think that's true, but I also think we need to make sure we're clear about what it means. I think there is no half-human, half-animal creature that was part of our evolution from apes. But it's hard to look at Lucy and the rest of that list above and say that there were never creatures that had characteristics of both living humans and living apes. In other words, there are creatures that might look kind of like intermediates, and if I were inclined to accept evolution, then I could see why people would think that these are our ancestors.

I know that's hard to read. It's hard to write. It's traitorous, really, like confessing a murder. I'm basically conceding that evolutionary theory successfully predicted the existence of intermediate forms. There really are things that look sort of like "missing links." It's not just humans either. There are dinosaurs with feathers that sort of look like they could be the ancestors of birds. There are reptiles that have jaws like mammals that sort of look like they could be the ancestors of mammals. There are fossil whales with hind legs that sort of look like they could be the ancestors of modern whales. There are even fish with bony fins that sort of look like they could be the ancestors of all the bony land animals. The list goes on and on and on.

Take a Deep Breath

So what do we do about these intermediate fossils? First of all, *don't panic*. Too many people get to this point and flip out. They feel like they've been lied to and that evolution is true after all! Or maybe they feel like I'm the liar and maybe I've been duped into believing in evolution! Maybe Jesus is all a lie! Or maybe I'm a wolf in sheep's clothing! Danger! DANGER!

Stop. Just stop. Don't panic. Take a deep breath, and think for a moment. What would José de Acosta do?

Acosta grew up knowing all about the global flood and how Noah saved all the kinds of animals in the ark. He had a really tough time explaining how all those people and unique creatures in South America could have gotten there from Noah's ark. He didn't know about the geography of Alaska and the genetic relationships between different people groups. He knew for sure that there were people in South America and that the voyage across the Atlantic Ocean was long and difficult. When it came to whether someone could cross the equator or live in the southern hemisphere, Acosta was willing to examine and even correct old beliefs, but he did it carefully and deliberately. He spent years thinking about these questions, and there were some questions he never could solve.

So what would Acosta do with intermediate forms, these supposed "missing links?" I think one thing he might do is look back to the scripture to make sure he got his beliefs right. After all, it's at least possible that we made a mistake in our understanding of scripture. We can't claim that we're infallible, right? Let's start there.

The creation of animals and people is recorded in the first chapters of Genesis. Especially in chapter one, we see God deliberately creating animals starting on the fifth day of creation week. Flying things and swimming things[16] appear on day five, and a day later all the land animals show up. Each group of animals is created "according to its kind." At the end of the author's description of the sixth day, God creates human beings, not according to their kind but in his own image. The story is pretty straightforward, and it's easy to understand. And there's not a hint of evolution from previously-existing animal ancestors.

If Genesis 1 were the only passage in the Bible that talked about human creation, I could imagine that more Christians might reasonably disagree over its interpretation. Even though its meaning seems pretty obvious, I could still imagine someone arguing that all of Genesis 1 was just a metaphor, allegory, or parable. But Genesis 1 is just the beginning (literally and figuratively).

The subsequent chapters describe the origin of humanity in much greater detail, including the Lord's careful crafting of Adam's body from the dust of the ground. Adam and Eve then broke God's one prohibitive command to abstain from the tree of the knowledge of good and evil, resulting in God's curse on creation. In the New Testament, the apostle Paul would explain that this original sin of Adam was the reason that Jesus Christ had to come to earth and die. Paul wrote to the Romans,

> Therefore, just as sin came into the world through one man, and death through sin, and so death spread to all men because all sinned... But the free gift is not like the trespass. For if many died through one man's trespass, much more have the grace of God and the free gift by the grace of that one man Jesus Christ abounded for many. ... For if, because of one man's trespass, death reigned through that one man, much more will those who receive the abundance of grace and the free gift of righteousness reign in life through the one man Jesus Christ. Therefore, as one trespass led to condemnation for all men, so one act of righteousness leads to justification and life for all men. For as by the one man's disobedience the many were made sinners, so by the one man's obedience the many will be made righteous. (Romans 5:12, 15, 17-19).

Paul made a similar point in his first letter to the Corinthians:

> For as by a man came death, by a man has come also the resurrection of the dead. For as in Adam all die, so also in Christ shall all be made alive (I Corinthians 15:21-22).

In the beginning, when the sum of humanity existed only as Adam and Eve, their sin, which God promised would bring death, did indeed bring death and suffering and guilt upon all people, who continued their forefather's sinful ways. Jesus Christ's resurrection from the dead defeated the death that Adam brought. Christ literally and bodily rose from the grave, just like Adam literally and bodily went to the grave *because of his sin.*

Paul is crystal clear on this point, and the church fathers unanimously agreed. When we examine the earliest generations of Christians who left written records after the New Testament, we find a complete affirmation of Paul's teaching. Jesus Christ died and rose again to undo the curse brought upon humanity by the fall of Adam and Eve. This notion of Adam's original sin has been a basic part of Christian identity from the beginning of Christianity.

And now we have evolution, which tells us that there was no special origin of humanity. There was no time when our ancestors numbered less than thousands. And there was definitely no time when our ancestors didn't experience death, just like we do. Don't believe them? Check out all those intermediate forms!

On the one hand, evolution seems kind of enticing, doesn't it? We can quibble about whether this or that fossil is a good representation of the animal ancestors of humans, but on the whole, the existence of these intermediate forms sure does look like a kind of evolution. On the other hand, we have two thousand years of Christian history, testimonies of lives radically changed by the power of God in Christ Jesus, and the theological identity handed down to us in a chain of Christian thought and writing back to the apostles and Jesus Himself. Hopefully, you can point to your own life and see God at work there too.

Now What?

So what do we do? There's that question again. On the one hand we have science that seems so powerful and persuasive, and on the other hand, we have a strong tradition of faith and a personal history with our redeemer. We have two reliable witnesses, but their testimony is very different. I think we have a couple of options, and I think Acosta would agree.

First, we could re-examine the Bible one more time. I don't know if that's going to do much for us here, but it never hurts to read the Bible, right? Let's say for the time being though that we've understood the scripture correctly. Now what?

Second, we could reject the Bible. Honestly, I think that's drastic and wrong. I pray that you do, too. God has been faithful and showered me with undeserved grace and kindness in my life, and I am fully convinced that he will continue to do so in the resurrection, when I see him face to face. Abandoning the faith is not an option.

Third, we could reject the science. This is attractive to a lot of people, especially those who might not understand all the details. I don't want to discount this option for individuals who really aren't trained in science. If thinking or learning about human evolution makes you upset, don't do it. That's easy, right? On the other hand, that's a terrible strategy for the church as a whole. Science has a great deal of cultural power in our modern world, and science has been immensely successful in many ways. We don't want to just reject it outright, and I don't think we should even discount its testimony, even on human evolution. Like it or not, science is credible even if it's not always right, and we as the church, the body of Christ, need to take it seriously.

Fourth, we can hold fast to our confession that God's Word is true and conclude that there must be some sense to be made of the natural world in the light of the Bible. In other words, the conflict that we see must be in our heads. We're ignorant, or we've made a mistake. I've already mentioned that we could re-examine the Bible, but we can also re-examine the science as well. That can be very difficult, of course, because science requires such specialized training and knowledge. Nevertheless, this is a clear way forward on our quest to understand: We acknowledge that there is a truth to be found that includes both our experience with God and our experience with creation (that's the goal of our quest), and we commit to finding it.

Is that realistic? Can we really figure this stuff out? Or am I just being arrogant? We'll talk about that in the next chapter.

ADOREMUS 2

In Genesis 11 we read the story of humanity after the flood, still reeling in fear of God's judgment, building a tower to reach the heavens. They wanted to make a name for themselves, a monument to remember them, a futile act of hubris. When God confused and scattered them, their tower was lost to history except for these few words in Genesis.

God, of course, made his own towers not of baked brick and mortar, but of living, breathing cells. These towers start life as tiny seedlings that shoot up sixty feet or more in just twenty years. They can reach over 350 feet tall, ninety feet around at the base, and more than a thousand years old. They are the coast redwoods of northwestern California.

Redwoods anchor themselves with shallow roots spread far beyond the tree to gather as much moisture as they can. The dense, ruddy bark protects the tree from insect invaders and fungal infection. The bark grows a foot thick and resists even fire. Burned trees have been known to grow new bark over scar tissue. Redwood leaves are stubby little needles, only a half inch long. At the very top of the tree, the needles grow as scales hugging the twigs and branches and limbs.

The redwoods thrive in a narrow strip stretching more than four hundred miles from Big Sur to the Oregon state line, never more than fifty miles inland. There, the temperature is cool, the rain is heavy, and the fog is thick. In the drier summer months, redwoods alter their own environments by providing water to themselves and the rest of the plants beneath them. As fog rolls in from the coast, water condenses on the redwood branches and needles. Condensation then drips to the ground, sometimes so densely it seems like rain. Understory plants can get as much as two thirds of their water from this redwood fog rain.[17]

With their dizzying height, redwoods draw our attention upward and point us to their great Builder. Unlike the tower of Babel built to magnify human arrogance, redwoods tower over the landscape as a testament to the power and greatness of the creator.

> *The name of the Lord is a strong tower;*
> *the righteous man runs into it and is safe.*
> *(Proverbs 18:10)*

3
ENCOUNTER
THE ALMIGHTY

In 1859, Charles Robert Bree finished his medical degree at the age of 48 and took a position at the Essex and Colchester Hospital in eastern England. That same year, the first volume of his massive *A History of the Birds of Europe, not observed in the British Isles* appeared, published by Groombridge & Sons in London. In November of 1859, Charles Darwin's *Origin of Species* was also released for the first time to the general public.

Dr. Bree was not impressed.

Barely a year later, Bree published his response in a lengthy book entitled *Species not Transmutable nor the Result of Secondary Causes*, which he evidently wrote in just the few months after *Origin* was published. In his preface, he disavowed any strong feelings about the book despite "the strong language I have sometimes felt bound to use." Strong language, indeed.

> From beginning to end the book is a cheerless, gloomy narrative. It destroys every vestige of the beautiful from the mind, without replacing it with even a plausible or intelligent theory. It is the great mistake of the age in which we live, and I hope, for his own sake, and for those whose principles it is calculated to unsettle, that not only will the greater work, with which we are threatened, never

see the light, but that this will be speedily withdrawn from circulation.[18]

With the benefit of hindsight, we can see that Dr. Bree's reaction was not the typical reaction to *Origin of Species*. While Darwin's book certainly stirred up controversy, the debate did not rage long. By 1875, most of Darwin's peers conceded that evolution had probably taken place.[19]

Bree's reaction seems out of place. *Origin* persuaded many. It was neither embarrassing to Darwin nor a complete failure, as Bree predicted. Nevertheless, reactions like Bree's persisted well into the twentieth century and even to the present.[20] I can't tell you how many people I run into who casually dismiss evolution as nonscientific bunk. As I do with Bree, I often find that such folks don't really understand what they reject, but that diminishes none of their passion. I suspect some people reading this book (if they're still reading) are probably in the same boat. Evolution is bunk, and nothing I can write will change their minds.

What We Don't Know

I don't think that really matters a whole lot. If you think Bree is a genius or Darwin is disturbingly persuasive, we're all still in the same situation. We live here in a vast universe, larger than we can even begin to imagine, all set in place by a creator who lavishes us with his loving kindness. His creations declare his glory. The stars whisper his name. The rocks cry out in praise to him. Every living thing shines with the beauty of his wisdom and power.

And we understand only a tiny fraction. It's easy to lose sight of that because science has made such enormous progress over the past century. Thanks to the discovery of germs and antibiotics, hospitals became places of healing instead of houses of death. Thanks to amazing advances in engineering, we went from the very first airplanes to walking on the moon in just 66 years. When I was growing up, if I wanted to know something I had to go to a library and look it up in a book. Now, I carry in my pocket access to a library more massive than anything my home town could have ever dreamed of. Because much of this wonder seems so commonplace today, we lose sight of how new and fantastic it really is.

We also lose sight of how little we really understand. Those antibiotics that revolutionized medicine have now brought on a new crisis as bacteria have become resistant. Just like it was when my grandparents were kids, some infections have become impossible to treat. Scientists have managed to sequence the human genome, which was a big deal in my early career working in genomics, but we still know only the basic rudiments of how it works. Just in my lifetime, an entire class of gene was discovered that we knew nothing about when I was in high school. We claim to know so much, but what's waiting for us next? What will the next discovery bring?

That's true for everyone, whether you think Darwin was clever or a moron. We're just beginning to understand God's amazing creation, and that's where I want to go. That's what the quest is all about. It's not a quest to prove evolution wrong. It's not a quest to prove anything wrong. Obsessing over things that are wrong won't help you understand the truth, just like worrying about all the wrong turns won't get you any closer to your travel destination. I don't want my life defined by error. I don't want mistakes and falsehoods to dictate how I spend the time I have here on this earth. I just want to leave the errors behind and push forward towards God's truth. That is the quest.

I've preached this message about pursuing truth as our highest goal many times, and I've gotten resistance in two different forms. The first objection is that the culture is obsessed with falsehood, and we need to expose it for what it is. And that is completely correct. Jesus was well known for His condemnation of the hypocrisy of the religious leaders of his day. Those encumbered and deceived by error must be shown the truth.

That doesn't mean we become obsessed with the error, even if people won't admit it's an error. When Jesus sent out the disciples to minister to villages in Israel, he encouraged them to move along if the people wouldn't listen. "And if anyone will not receive you or listen to your words, shake off the dust from your feet when you leave that house or town. Truly, I say to you, it will be more bearable on the day of judgment for the land of Sodom and Gomorrah than for that town" (Matthew 10:14-15). Just move on to the next village. Life is too short to obsess over those who refuse to hear.

The other objection I get is more challenging. How can we ever think that we can understand God's creation? Isn't that just arrogance? Isn't that the error of the evolutionists? They think they're so smart, making up their stories about how living things came to be. Why would we ever want to be like that? We'd be just as wrong as they are.

Some have even taken this objection a step further: Because we human beings are utterly fallen, our minds are completely corrupted by sin. We are incapable of understanding God's ways unless he directly reveals them to us. Since God didn't reveal the mysteries of creation to us in the Bible, we shouldn't expect to be able to really understand it in the way that I want to understand it.

I could add to that objection one more of my own making: Skeptical questioning is a slippery slope. If we're going to turn a skeptical eye on matters of faith, where do we stop? How can we really claim to have certain knowledge if faith is involved? Frankly, the same could be said of skeptical thinking itself. If we're skeptical about skeptical thinking (which we could be), then where do we stop? How can we know anything? If we start this quest with critical thinking, we may end up in some post-modern despair of ever knowing anything at all. Where do we stop?

As a Christian, I think we have a good place to stop in this crisis of skepticism: God himself, and most importantly, my own experiences with him. Let me make that perfectly clear. The reason I'm not a rampant skeptic, a Richard Dawkins-style scoffer, is because of my own personal, purely subjective, non-transferable experiences with the risen Lord Jesus Christ, my savior. This isn't anything I can logically defend. It is my own experience. Yours may be different. I can't account for your experiences, but I know what mine are.

This is where I probably part company with a large part of our logic-worshiping society. "You can't base your thinking on subjectivity! It's not logical! You're being irrational! You can't have a conversation with someone else who thinks differently if you're going to rely on personal experience!" I've heard it all before, and I don't believe any of it.

Frankly, we all begin with the subjective. We all have to make certain decisions about how we will interpret the world around us.

Call them biases, assumptions, worldview, or whatever, but you can't even begin to think about the world without them, even if you don't know you have them. Even folks who claim that everything we do must be objective and rational are making a choice. They might have good reasons for doing so, but it's still their own subjective choice. I also think I have good reasons for recognizing the hand of God in my life, even though it is my own subjective experience.

Job's Encounter

Thousands of years ago, there was a man in the land of Uz whose name was Job. He was a very good man. He worshipped God and avoided evil. In the midst of his righteous living, Job experienced an unspeakable calamity. In a single day, he lost all his material goods, the source of his food and his livelihood, and all ten of his children were senselessly murdered. After a period of mourning, Job began asking for the opportunity to plead his case before God.

After all, rationality tells us that bad things happen to *bad* people, and Job hadn't done anything wrong. Job's friends disagreed. They insisted that he must have done something pretty terrible that he wouldn't admit, but Job knew better. Job knew he was innocent. Job was on his own quest for understanding. He wanted to understand why he suffered.

The big surprise came when God showed up ready to talk with Job directly. It wasn't exactly what Job was hoping for, though, because God showed up in a whirlwind, and he basically told Job, "Who do you think you are? I'm going to ask the questions now!" From there, the Lord asked question after question, all of which are still awkward and uncomfortable today. He started with,

> Where were you when I laid the foundation of the earth?
> Tell me, if you have understanding.
> Who determined its measurements—surely you know!
> Or who stretched the line upon it?
> On what were its bases sunk,
> or who laid its cornerstone,
> when the morning stars sang together
> and all the sons of God shouted for joy?
> (Job 38:4-7)

It doesn't get much better after that. God kept firing off these impossible questions, and Job was at a loss for words. Who can blame him? I would be, too!

It's ironic that Job so desperately wanted to plead his case directly to God, to explain the rational, logical reasons why he should not be suffering, but all that logic and rationality went right out the door when God appeared. After his encounter with the Almighty, Job managed to say only,

> I know that you can do all things,
> and that no purpose of yours can be thwarted.
> "Who is this that hides counsel without knowledge?"
> Therefore I have uttered what I did not understand,
> things too wonderful for me, which I did not know.
> "Hear, and I will speak;
> I will question you, and you make it known to me."
> I had heard of you by the hearing of the ear,
> but now my eye sees you;
> therefore I despise myself,
> and repent in dust and ashes.
> (Job 42:2-6)

That fiery speaker who wanted to defend himself with rationality and logic was radically changed by this personal encounter with God. I suspect that God was the real object of his quest anyway. Job never really wanted answers, not deep down. After all, what kind of answer to "Why did my ten children have to be murdered?" would ever be satisfying? Can you imagine God explaining to Job the divine bet with the devil? I imagine Job raising an eyebrow and saying, "Yes, I see, Lord. That *is* a good reason! Well done!" No, that's ridiculous. Job wasn't going to be satisfied with answers, but he was transformed by the presence of God.

Now let's play twenty-first century skeptic for a moment: Job was on a crusade to right a cruel injustice, and he was dissuaded from this by a talking tornado? Really? Okay, sure, that's totally irrational. But it's not. It's not irrational at all. It's completely beyond rationality or logic. How do you even put into words an encounter with the living Creator of the universe, the Lord of Hosts, the Almighty God? Job said, "Behold, I am of small account; what shall I answer you? I lay my hand on my mouth" (Job 40:4). Job knew exactly what to do.

Faith, Knowledge, and Fideism

So I want to take my stand with Job and all the other saints of the Old and New Testament who found themselves radically and completely changed by a brush with the Almighty. There's absolutely nothing about that choice to be ashamed of. Jesus' sheep hear his voice and they know him and they follow him. And in that little act of foolish following, God defeats all the wisdom of the world, and true wisdom—his wisdom—finally begins.

To me, this is faith, not that I'm convinced by evidence but I'm convinced by a person. The modern, scientific world sees things differently, of course. They want me to obsess over the importance of external, scientific evidence for the Bible or the logic and rationality of theism. Some have looked at my faith and called me a *fideist*, which is a fancy philosophical word for a person who believes that knowledge comes only through faith. Unlike me, the fideist believes that evidence cannot lead us to knowledge. I believe that we can make sense of evidence. Why else would I be a scientist? But at the end of the day, I also recognize the deeply personal experience of God that drives me and my quest. The word *rationality* doesn't even begin to describe those divine encounters.

The fear of the Lord is the beginning of wisdom. Don't let anyone tell you otherwise. Don't be bullied into thinking you have to conform your beliefs to the world's idea of a rational or logical or defensible deity. The quest, if it is to be anything other than chasing the wind, must be a quest *for God*, wherever he may be found. Sometimes he might be found in a wonderful research project that confirms some aspect of his creation. More often, though, I've encountered him in the smallest, most inconsequential details that only I notice. I can't explain them. I can't make sense of them. But they are precious to me. They remind me that he is here with me in my quest. It's not crazy, and it's not impossible.

Don't fall into the despair of cruel rationality or endless skepticism. We can encounter God. That's a great place to start.

ADOREMUS 3

Three hundred species of flitting, glittering nectar drinkers spread across two vast continents. These tiniest of all birds beat their wings fast enough to float in the middle of the air, like a bee or a bug. At nine inches long, the giant hummingbird is the largest of these miniscule fliers, but she still weighs less than an ounce full grown. The tiniest of the tiny, the bee hummingbird of Cuba, grows a little longer than two inches. The entire body of that bird, from beak to tail, is smaller than your pinky finger.

Each hummingbird eats flower nectar, when they're not eating bugs, spiders, or other tiny critters that cross their paths. Some hummingbirds even have beaks specially shaped to fit right into particular flowers. Like all such relationships, the flowers reproduce by feeding hummingbirds. As the hummingbirds lap up the sugary nectar the flowers make just for them, they also move pollen from one flower to another, and so a new generation of flowers is made.

The visual artistry of the hummingbird lies in its plumage. Surprisingly, the dizzying array of colors in hummingbirds are not pigments but microscopic textures on the feathers. The textures hold layer on layer of air bubbles, all of which interact with light to absorb or amplify different colors. As you turn your eyes, as the hummingbird darts and dives through your vision, the colors seem to change because of these textures on their wings. This is iridescence, and it is exquisite.

Though unknown to the authors of scripture, the hummingbirds are perfectly known to the author of creation. Their elegance reflects the glory of the creator. Their speed and grace reveal the wonder and majesty of our savior's most delicate designs. Even these smallest, most insignificant birds wear a beauty greater than Solomon in all his glory. If this is how our heavenly father cares for the birds, which are here today and gone tomorrow, will he not also care for you, oh you of little faith?

And do not fear those who kill the body but cannot kill the soul. Rather fear him who can destroy both soul and body in hell. Are not two sparrows sold for a penny? And not one of them will fall to the ground apart from your Father. Fear not, therefore; you are of more value than many sparrows. (Matthew 10:28-29, 31)

4
GALILEO READS THE BIBLE

If the quest can begin with a personal encounter with God, how do we move from that encounter to understanding what God is telling us about creation? Can we really turn to the pages of scripture to understand the mysteries of creation? If we can, what does the scripture say? Scholars have debated these questions for centuries, from the time of the scientific revolution. To understand how modern scholars approach these questions, I need to tell you a story.

The Medicis

It was a Wednesday morning in Pisa, near the western coast of what is today Italy, and Benedetto Castelli was having a chat with the Grand Duke of Tuscany. Castelli gave a detailed report on the state of the University of Pisa, where Castelli was a mathematics professor. The Grand Duke was pleased with the report, and the conversation then turned to the latest curiosity of the day, the telescope. Castelli confirmed that he did indeed own a telescope, and he then began describing the "Medicean planets," which we now know as Europa, Callisto, Ganymede, and Io, the four largest moons of Jupiter. These moons had been discovered only three years previously, and they had been named after the house of Medici, the most powerful and influential family in nearby Florence. The Grand Duke himself was Cosimo II de' Medici.

At this point, their conversation turned to the other hot topic of the day: Did the sun orbit the earth, or did the earth orbit the sun? The Grand Duke's mother, Christina of Lorraine, asked Castelli if the Medicean planets were real and not just a trick of the telescope. Castelli replied that they were indeed real, and Cosimo Boscaglia agreed with him. Boscaglia was a professor of philosophy and another favorite of the Grand Duke, and even though he accepted the existence of Jupiter's moons, he vocally denied the movement of the earth. According to Boscaglia, the idea that the earth orbited the sun contradicted the clear teaching of the Bible.

Castelli remained silent on this point, having been warned by his boss at the university not to debate the structure of the cosmos. The subject had become a point of contentious debate, and too many felt as Boscaglia did. The earth could not move, nor could the sun be the center of the cosmos. These ideas were supposedly contrary to scripture, and the overseer of the University of Pisa was keen to avoid stirring up trouble on this matter. Castelli assured him that he would not engage the topic, and he was true to his word on that Wednesday with the Medicis.

As he was leaving, a servant of Christina's called him back. The Grand Duchess wanted to talk further about the Bible and the motion of the earth. You can imagine how Castelli must have felt at this summons, but he went back anyway. He found himself in a room facing Cosimo II, his wife Archduchess Maria Maddalena, the Grand Duchess Christina, and, of course, Dr. Boscaglia.

What followed was a spirited theological defense of the motion of the earth, after Castelli gave "suitable disclaimers," which we may surmise might have been a confession that he only presented the defense for the sake of argument. By his own account, Castelli convinced those in the room, including the Grand Duke and Archduchess, but the Grand Duchess Christina continued to question him. What Christina really believed we don't know for sure. Castelli got the impression that she was just playing devil's advocate to see how he would answer. Ominously, Boscaglia remained silent during the entire discussion.[21]

Sensing trouble from this encounter with the Medicis, Castelli wrote almost immediately to his good friend Galileo Galilei to describe the conversation. Galileo had discovered Jupiter's moons in January of 1610, and Galileo gave them the name "Medicean planets," in honor of his former student and benefactor, Cosimo II. Galileo was also the chief instigator of the debate over the motion of the earth, stirring the pot most recently with a treatise on sunspots, in which he reported the existence of spots on the sun that moved as the sun rotated. This contradicted the traditional belief that the sun was flawless and unmoving. Castelli's letter would spur Galileo once more to defend his belief that the earth moved around the sun.

Galileo began working on a letter directly to the Grand Duchess herself, explaining how he could hold to the motion of the earth around the sun and make sense of the Bible at the same time. The *Letter to the Grand Duchess Christina* became Galileo's most enduring contribution to the faith/science discussion and the tipping point in his ongoing dispute with theological authorities.[22] The ideas expressed in this letter were submitted to the Inquisition (in the form of an early draft sent directly to Castelli), who warned Galileo less than three years later not to believe or teach that the earth moves or the sun is the center of the cosmos.

Galileo's Accommodation

What was in the *Letter to the Grand Duchess*? Galileo began with a simple affirmation of the truth of scripture, but he qualified that affirmation with what seems to be a reasonable caution.

> I believe nobody will deny that it is often very abstruse, and may say things which are quite different from what its bare words signify. Hence in expounding the Bible if one were always to confine oneself to the unadorned grammatical meaning, one might fall into error. Not only contradictions and propositions far from true might thus be made to appear in the Bible, but even grave heresies and follies. Thus it would be necessary to assign to God feet, hands, and eyes....[23]

Why does this happen? Why isn't scripture more clear and understandable? Galileo had an answer.

> These propositions uttered by the Holy Ghost were set
> down in that manner by the sacred scribes in order to
> accommodate them to the capacities of the common
> people, who are rude and unlearned. For the sake of those
> who deserve to be separated from the herd, it is necessary
> that wise expositors should produce the true senses of
> such passages, together with the special reasons for which
> they were set down in these words. This doctrine is so
> widespread and so definite with all theologians that it
> would be superfluous to adduce evidence for it.[24]

Accommodation is Galileo's answer. Not everything in the Bible
can be taken literally because sometimes the Holy Spirit used figures
of speech or metaphors to communicate truths that were hard for
people to understand. The Bible is accommodated to everyone so
we can all understand.

I like to explain it by comparing our intellect to God's. God is
infinite and omniscient. His understanding is far above ours, and
compared to God's, our intellect is barely different from an ant's. Or
maybe a piece of driveway gravel. For God to reveal himself to us,
he must speak in language that we can understand, and the human
language that he uses includes all those figures of speech. He has to
talk to us the way we talk.

Now there's nothing wrong with accommodation. It's a
theological necessity, but Galileo took the idea one step further.
Galileo concluded that because the Bible is accommodated, we can
never use the Bible to tell us anything about the physical reality of
creation.

> This [accommodation] being granted, I think that in
> discussions of physical problems we ought to begin
> not from the authority of scriptural passages, but from
> sense-experiences and necessary demonstrations.... It
> is necessary for the Bible, in order to be accommodated
> to the understanding of every man, to speak many things
> which appear to differ from the absolute truth so far as the
> bare meaning of the words is concerned. But Nature, on
> the other hand, is inexorable and immutable; she never

transgresses the laws imposed upon her, or cares a whit whether her abstruse reasons and methods of operation are understandable to men. For that reason it appears that nothing physical which sense-experience sets before our eyes, or which necessary demonstrations prove to us, ought to be called in question (much less condemned) upon the testimony of biblical passages which may have some different meaning beneath their words.[25]

We need to pay attention very carefully to what Galileo says here. Galileo claims that the Bible is hard to understand, and its words may be interpreted in many different ways. Creation, on the other hand, and science in particular, is essentially infallible. When science speaks on a subject, that settles it. If the Bible seems to contradict science, the Bible must be accommodated on that point. We only need to discover the true meaning beneath the words, because what it says cannot be what it means, because science says otherwise.

With this interpretive maneuver, Galileo essentially set aside *all* biblical and theological objections against his ideas about the motion of the earth around the sun. None of them have any weight or force behind them, because the Bible might be accommodated when it talks about the sun and the earth. There is no room in Galileo's model for careful exegesis to determine what the biblical text might be saying as a corrective or boundary for science. No, science is the deciding factor. If science says something, the Bible must be re-interpreted to fit.

My description of accommodation is unsettling and often upsetting to modern theistic evolutionists. They do not like such blunt talk, and they do not want to admit that they are re-interpreting scripture according to the dictates of science. Yet, that is precisely what Galileo argues in his *Letter to the Grand Duchess*, and it's hard to argue that that is not happening today. The recent and steady parade of books describing the textual and theological gymnastics that evangelical scholars must perform to fit evolution into the Bible speaks for itself.[26]

Galileo's accommodation is everywhere in the faith/science discussion today, especially when it comes to evolution. When the theory of evolution appeared in the nineteenth century, religious leaders and scholars who did not immediately condemn it very much wanted to wait and see how the scientific debate would turn out.[27] No one wanted to repeat Galileo's fate of being forced into a humiliating rejection of his own beliefs about the cosmos by a church that was ultimately just wrong. Even now, no one wants to be Galileo, and no one wants to be the church that condemned him.

Accommodating Evolution

How do we reconcile evolution and the Bible? Supposedly by accommodation. As the story goes, God performed a loving act of kindness by accommodating the story of creation (which was really evolution) to the myths of ancient Sumer, Canaan, and Egypt so that the Israelites could see how their God was different. The pagan gods were many, but the true God was one. The pagan gods created through war and conflict, but the true God absolutely controlled every step of creation. The pagan gods created out of the chaos of a world that already existed. The true God created everything with no hint of chaos. These are the great truths of Genesis. The details, which seem so plainly historical, are all just accommodated. The dust of the ground, the talking serpent, the forbidden fruit—they're all just parables or figures of speech. In our modern world, as science has opened our eyes to the truth about evolution, we can finally see what the true meaning of the Bible was all along.

Does that really work, though? Can we really believe that the only true meaning of Genesis is not found in the details and the words of the text but in the theological content it was supposed to convey? To put it simply, would God accommodate his revelation to cultural error?

As I said, I completely affirm accommodation as a general principle, because language is full of phrases and words that do not mean what they appear to mean. Even today, anyone with an internet connection can find detailed tables describing the time of sunrise and sunset, even though we all know that the sun isn't really moving. The earth is turning. The sun only appears to "rise" and "set." This is one of the reasons that I think Galileo's critics were wrong. I think accommodation in that instance works just fine. When the Bible describes the motion of the sun, it uses the same sort of language our modern culture does with all our knowledge of the universe. We talk about the motion of the sun because that's what it looks like, and so does the Bible. God's revelation is unquestionably accommodated to figures of speech.

But does that mean God accommodates error? What if the Bible contained a passage that detailed the structure of the cosmos and described in unmistakable detail the motion of the sun around the earth? Or what if the Bible contained a treatise on anatomy and physiology that endorsed the old idea of the doctrine of the humors? Or a treatise on physics that listed the four elements earth, wind, fire, and air? Is that something God would do?

Because if evolution is true and Genesis is accommodated, that is exactly what God did. He took erroneous ideas about the origin of the universe and wrote them right into the text of the Bible. He could have revealed this theology in another way. Several creation psalms and even the end of Job present God as the absolute, unrivaled creator and sustainer of the universe without telling any detailed story about creation. He didn't have to tell a series of creation fables, but he did. He preserved them for thousands of years, and all the while, his followers assumed they were historical and not fables at all. He knew that one day we would discover the "truth" about evolution, and he knew that that discovery would cause a great crisis of faith that continues to this day. And he knew that the discovery would come at a time when the population of the world was the greatest and communication was most sophisticated so that the greatest number of people would be offended and fall away because of evolutionary science. With all that knowledge, he did it anyway. He included a myth at the beginning of the Bible knowing that Christians for millennia would interpret it as a historical account of the origin of the world and knowing the havoc that would ensue when the truth was discovered.

Does that sound like a God who loves truth? Does that sound like a God who loves people? Or does that sound like a cruel and deceptive god who sets up the human race in a cosmic prank that would alienate millions? Maybe even billions? I know my God, and I do not recognize the great trickster god of evolution. That is not my God. My God recorded the history of creation in Genesis precisely because he knew that one day we would misunderstand the works of creation in the hubris of the scientific revolution. He lovingly and carefully preserved for us the truth about creation. In the beginning, God created, and it was very good.

If accommodation to error is wrong, what then can we say about the creation of everything? What should we conclude from the first eleven chapters of Genesis? Do we have to ignore hundreds of years of scientific research, effectively sticking our heads in the sand, in order to be "good Christians?" Is that really what God wants?

ADOREMUS 4

Tiny and transparent, almost unnoticed, roundworms wriggle through decomposing organic material—dead leaves, mushrooms, other small animals—feeding on the decay and the bacteria it attracts. At less than a millimeter long, these unnoticed worms have no common name, despite occurring in just about every temperate environment the world over. They're known mostly to curious scientists who went looking for them, and scientists call them Caenorhabditis. *If that's a mouthful for you, try this: SEE-no-rab-DIE-tiss. Or just call them wormies. Whatever works for you.*

Caenorhabditis *are roundworms. Mostly gut and gonads, they have no heart or lungs. Though brainless, their simple nervous system controls four bands of muscles that produce the wriggling motion. They undulate up and down as they move, and their heads produce the finer movements that direct them right or left. They are simple, little wormies.*

And we know more about these little wormies than we know about any other animal. Scientists have studied Caenorhabditis *intensely since the 1960s. We know that there are precisely 959 cells in almost every adult body (except the very rare adult male, which has 1031 cells), and we know exactly how each of those cells developed from the fertilized worm egg.[28] About a third of those cells, 302 to be precise, are neurons.[29] Scientists have discovered about 20,000 genes in the worm,[30] and they've mapped precisely when and where each gene is active during the worm's development.*[31]

I could go on and on about these little wormies, but I'd have to use even more technical jargon that no one would understand. Instead, we can just sum them all up by saying that we know a lot about Caenorhabditis. As Paul reminds us in his first letter to the Corinthians, knowledge puffs up. At least, human knowledge puffs up.

Few things humble us more than realizing our six decades of work deciphering the mysteries of Caenorhabditis taught us nothing that God didn't already know. In fact, that time has only revealed to us a design plan that he invented in the first place, and that's just one worm. Scientists figure there are millions of different species on this planet, each with their own amazing designs just waiting for someone to discover. There are more wonders in this creation than there are people to find them. It is the glory of God to conceal a matter, but it is the glory of kings to seek a matter out.

God also knows you. More amazing than the design of a tiny worm, God has a design for your life. According to the letter to the Ephesians, God sent Jesus not just to save us but to turn us into his own masterpieces of virtue and righteousness. We are remade in Christ Jesus to walk in good works that God has already designed for our lives. He is worthy of our praise and our worship and our devotion.

O Lord, you have searched me and known me!
You know when I sit down and when I rise up;
you discern my thoughts from afar.
You search out my path and my lying down
and are acquainted with all my ways.
Even before a word is on my tongue,
behold, O Lord, you know it altogether.
You hem me in, behind and before,
and lay your hand upon me.
Such knowledge is too wonderful for me;
it is high; I cannot attain it.
Search me, O God, and know my heart!
Try me and know my thoughts!
And see if there be any grievous way in me,
and lead me in the way everlasting!
(Psalm 139:1-6, 23-24)

5
THE TESTIMONY
OF SCRIPTURE

Back when I worked at Bryan College, they hired a new Old Testament professor. Hiring new Bible professors was always kind of an anxious time for me, since Old Testament was part of my work there in the former Center for Origins Research. Whenever the college hired new Bible professors or administrators, I always prayed that we would get one that would support our work at the Center. I'd heard too many horror stories of creationists being harassed (or worse) when new faculty smuggled in personal hostility toward creationists. This new guy was okay though. He'd heard some bad rumors about creationists in the past, but he really appreciated what we were doing. So we hit it off.

After a while, he and I chatted about what Bible scholars might be able to contribute to young-age creationism, and I rattled off a huge list of questions I had. Some he answered right away, and some he said he'd have to look into. At one point I tried to explain my view on creation, miracles, and the laws of physics. First of all, the Bible teaches that creation ended on the seventh day (God "finished his work," Genesis 2:2). Because of that teaching, I assumed that there was no more creation after that point. Any miracle that appeared to create something new was merely a rearrangement of matter that was already created. After all, physics tells us that matter can neither be created nor destroyed. If creation was finished, then miracles after creation could only manipulate the matter that already existed.

He frowned and asked me, "What do you do with the feeding of the five thousand?"

"Well," I replied, "I assume that while Jesus was multiplying the fish on the shore, there were fish in the Sea of Galilee that were disappearing."

He stared at me for a moment. "That's really weird," he said. Then he burst out laughing.

I laughed too, that awkward laugh you laugh when you realize you've said something really stupid, and you want to pretend it was all a joke. It wasn't a joke, though. I really thought that.

That conversation really stuck with me, and I think it taught me a pretty important lesson about being careful with the Bible. I had believed that bit about the conservation of matter for years, and in one second, the hilarious reaction of an actual Bible scholar made me realize that I'd had it all wrong. I needed my thoughts about the Bible to be better.

The Quest to Understand the Bible

See, that's a big myth about creationists. Our critics, including theistic evolutionists, look at us and think that we just take every word of the Bible literally. For them, it seems like their only alternative to Galileo's accommodation is sort of a bone-headed, ham-fisted literalism. They wonder why we don't stone disobedient children or butcher cities full of Canaanites. I'm not kidding, either. I've talked to more theistic evolutionists than I can count, and they don't understand us at all. They definitely don't understand how we view the Bible.

But understanding the Bible is part of the quest. The Bible is not always clear, and it's definitely not clear on a lot of points I'd like to know. Just because I'm a creationist doesn't mean I always understand every little detail of Genesis. I don't know that any creationist does.

For example, what in the world are the nephilim? Genesis 6 tells us,

> When man began to multiply on the face of the land and daughters were born to them, the sons of God saw that the daughters of man were attractive. And they took as their

wives any they chose. ... The Nephilim were on the earth in those days, and also afterward, when the sons of God came in to the daughters of man and they bore children to them. These were the mighty men who were of old, the men of renown. (Genesis 6:1-2,4)

There are two ways that this text has been interpreted. One interpretation is that the "sons of God" are fallen angels and the "daughters of men" are human. Their offspring, the nephilim, are demon-human hybrids. The other option is less sensational. The "sons of God" are the godly descendants of Seth, and the "daughters of men" are the wicked descendants of Cain. The intermarrying is a sign of the corruption of the godly family of Seth, setting the stage for the spreading of wickedness to all humanity.

I personally like the idea of the Cainites and Sethites mingling. It reminds me of God's warning Israel not to mingle with the Canaanites, and frankly, the idea of demon-human hybrids sounds like something from a bad horror movie. Imagine my surprise when I discovered that these two interpretations are at least as old as Christianity itself.[32] No one has ever agreed on what this passage means. It is a mystery.

There are other open questions as well.

- How does a snake talk? Was that normal in the Garden of Eden?

- There are 3,000 species of snakes today. Does the curse on the serpent apply to all of them? Or just one created kind of snakes? How many created kinds of snakes are there anyway?

- How should we understand the relationship of animal death and the fall?

- If people didn't eat meat until the flood, why did Abel keep the flocks?

- Why was Abel's sacrifice accepted, and Cain's rejected? Who told them to offer sacrifices anyway?

- Cain's family has a lot of technological firsts: First metalworkers, first musical instruments, first city. How do these technological accomplishments relate to the world after the flood?

- Why do the ages of the patriarchs in Genesis 5 and 11 end in a set of nonrandom digits? Are they rounded? If so, why?

- How did Noah know what clean and unclean animals were?

And that's just the start. I could go verse by verse and list a bunch of questions. To be fair, people have proposed answers to most of those questions, and I suspect that most creationists would not accept the relationship of animal death and the fall as an open question.

I think some people find it strange that I have so many open questions about the book of Genesis even though I still feel comfortable making a firm commitment to young-age creationism. Surely a guy with so many "doubts" should be more agnostic about the age of the earth and God's mode of creation! Right?

My friend who laughed at my disappearing fish interpretation taught me something else that I thought was very helpful. He used to tell me, "Be firm when the Bible is clear and be ambiguous where the Bible is ambiguous." So I take my stand on the clarity of scripture, but I'll always be open to exploring those unanswered questions.

I also don't think unanswered questions should be allowed to cause anxiety or doubt, precisely because we have the clarity of scripture and the power of our own experiences with the Lord. And if I have made a mistake about the Bible (disappearing fish), that's OK too. It's not the end of the world. Why should I let questions about the nephilim cause me to doubt the power of the resurrected Lord Jesus Christ?

The Clarity of Creation

What then is all this clarity in Genesis that inspires me to be a young-age creationist? Having studied this issue for years, I've come to recognize a three-fold witness to the historicity of Genesis 1-11: text, tradition, and theology.

First of all, I see in the text of the Bible ample reason to think that Genesis 1-11 is trying to describe real people and real events. For example, I don't see any clues or hints in the text that we're reading a parable. Jesus always gave us hints that he was talking in parables. He'd say, "There was a certain man…" or "The kingdom of heaven is like…" Those phrases were like a biblical "Once upon a time…" that lets the listener (and reader) know that the story they're about to hear is an illustration and not meant to be historical. The prophets also spoke in veiled and metaphoric imagery, and in those cases, there were other clues to the real meaning of the text. The prophets wrote in poetic form, and their language was full of rich—and obviously nonliteral—imagery. Often the Lord would just have the prophet declare to the people what their parables meant.

Genesis is different though. There's none of the regular hints that we're about to read a parable. Instead, we are presented with people living through some extraordinary circumstances (much like every other part of the Bible), and it runs straight into the history of Israel. There's an unbroken line from Adam to Abraham. The Bible does not present these stories as if they were parables.

The New Testament also seems to treat Genesis 1-11 as if it were historical. Jesus justified God's hatred of divorce by appealing to the creation of Adam and Eve (Matthew 19). Jesus mentioned the murder of Abel as if it were a real sin (Matthew 23:35; Luke 11:51). Jesus also compared the coming kingdom of God to the sudden onslaught of the flood (Matthew 24:37-38; Luke 17:26-27). Peter makes a similar comparison between the coming judgment and the flood (I Peter 3; II Peter 2). The faith chapter in Hebrews commends Abel, Enoch, and Noah as examples of faith. Perhaps most importantly, as we already discussed in chapter two, Paul refers to Adam's sin and links it directly to the death and resurrection of Jesus Christ.

Looking at the text as it is, I think it's fairly clear that the authors of scripture and the Holy Spirit that inspired them viewed the people and events of Genesis 1-11 as historical. These are not merely parables. There was a real Adam and Eve, a real Garden of Eden, and a real flood. These things happened.

The second major witness to the historicity of Genesis 1-11 is the Christian tradition. I understand that the word *tradition* is kind of a touchy subject for Protestants. After all, we're pretty big on the priesthood of the believer and the perspicuity of scripture. That means that the important parts of the Bible are open and accessible to anyone's understanding, and we don't need a priest or ecumenical council to explain it to us. Protestants don't give blind allegiance to tradition.

But do we need tradition? I think the Christian tradition does something incredibly valuable for us here in Genesis 1-11. Tradition can help us answer one big question: How would a Christian read Genesis 1-11 if they knew nothing about modern science?

A longstanding complaint from creationists is that all these strange, counterintuitive interpretations of Genesis being proposed by theistic evolutionists are manufactured only as a means of making the Bible fit evolution. The "accommodation" happening isn't God accommodating his revelation to the limits of human language and understanding, it's human beings trying to accommodate the Bible to an overreaching and unyielding science. In other words, pro-evolution bias is the driving force behind heterodox interpretations of Genesis. Take that bias away, and no one would ever read Genesis as anything other than history.[33]

Looking to the Christian tradition can help us test this. In the tradition, we find 1,500 years of biblical interpretation unhindered and untainted by the scientific revolution or Galileo's version of accommodation. So what do we find in this tradition?

First of all, the tradition is complicated, and it's complicated in one especially remarkable and fascinating way. Ancient authors, and especially medieval theologians, very often believed in multiple interpretations of the same passage. In fact, by the Middle Ages, theologians recognized four types of interpretation: literal, typological, moral, and anagogical.[34] The literal interpretation was the simplest of the four meanings. That's where you find the straightforward, historical meaning of the passage. The typological meaning tried to connect passages to the life and person of Jesus Christ, much like Hebrews connects Jesus to the Tabernacle and the priesthood. We might call this a figurative or allegorical interpretation. The moral meaning emphasized the application to ethics and right behavior. It was the "moral of the story." The anagogical meaning connected each passage prophetically to either the status of heaven or the coming kingdom. The word anagogical refers to a spiritual climb or ascent, and anagogical meanings raise our attention to heaven and God's kingdom. Any single author then could hold to multiple interpretations *at the same time*. The modern view of metaphorical interpretations *falsifying* historical readings is pretty unusual in Christian tradition. These weren't competing interpretations. They were all true of the same text.

This complicates things when consulting the tradition. If you don't understand how the ancient and medieval theologians discussed scripture, it's easy to find someone who agrees with your own bias. Are you a theistic evolutionist looking for an allegorical reading of Genesis? There are plenty in the tradition. Looking for something more along the lines of young-age creationism? There are plenty of those, too. As we encounter the tradition, then, we need to carefully examine whether the authors are explicitly denying the literal, historical sense of Genesis. Just citing allegorical readings is not enough.

For example, Origen of Alexandria was a famous Christian author of the third century. He lived in Egypt and produced a huge number of manuscripts, including sermons and even a text of the Hebrew Bible. His name today is largely synonymous with imaginative, allegorical interpretations of the Bible. He would be a great candidate for someone who did not accept the historicity of Genesis, but that doesn't seem to be what he thought. His second homily on Genesis contains a detailed discussion of the construction of Noah's ark, defending it against criticism that it could not be true history. He even mentions the disposal of animal waste:

> Certainly since Scripture related nothing about the places which we said were set apart for the excrement of the animals, but tradition preserves some things, it will appear opportune that silence has been maintained on this about which reason may sufficiently teach of its importance. And because it could less worthily be fitted to a spiritual meaning, rightly, therefore, Scripture, which rather fits its narratives to allegorical meanings, was silent about this.[35]

For Origen, history wasn't denied by the allegorical meaning of scripture. Instead, historical details of real events were selected for preservation in scripture for allegorical purposes. History was one layer of meaning and allegory another; neither one denied the other. It's a very different attitude than you'll find today.

What then does Christian tradition tell us? In every age of church history, Christian authors were concerned to affirm the historical details of Genesis 1-11. Not every author paid attention to the historicity of Genesis, but enough of them did so that we may assume that this was the default understanding of Genesis. Indeed, the crises that would come about after the Scientific Revolution further confirm that people understood Genesis 1-11 as a history of the origin of the world. No one would fuss about the age of the earth, the creation of species, or the person of Adam if they didn't think that Genesis was telling us something historical.

Finally and perhaps most importantly, theology also supports the historicity of Genesis 1-11. I once again point to the doctrine of Adam's fall, the curse on creation, and their connection to Christ's redemption as important and ancient features of Christian theology and identity. Looking to Christian tradition again, we find the full weight of the church fathers behind this understanding of a perfect creation, followed by a fall into sin and a cosmic curse, and finally the resurrection of Jesus as the firstfruits of the redemption of all creation. This is a central feature of Christian theology made possible by reading Genesis 3 as history.

Additionally, the historicity of Genesis touches on the doctrines of the inspiration and perspicuity of scripture. In his second epistle to Timothy, Paul claimed that "All scripture is breathed out by God" (II Timothy 3:16). The concept Paul wanted to communicate was so different and radical that he invented a new Greek word to express it, *theopneustos*, "God breathed." In the King James Version, the translators rendered it as "inspired." In his second epistle, Peter affirms the Old Testament by claiming that "no prophecy was ever produced by the will of man, but men spoke from God as they were carried along by the Holy Spirit" (II Peter 1:21). The Bible is not merely a human work of theology. The Bible is God's Word to us.

As I already mentioned, the Reformers denied the need for priests or popes to interpret the Bible for us. Instead, they affirmed that what we needed to know for salvation was clear in the Bible and understandable to anyone. This became the doctrine of perspicuity. My friend's statement that we should be firm where the Bible is clear is another form of that doctrine. When the Bible's meaning is clear, then that is authoritative, because the Bible is the Word of God.

When we consider inspiration and perspicuity on the question of creation and interpreting Genesis, I find very little theological justification for questioning the long-standing reading of Genesis as history. Instead, I find that Genesis 1-11 is mostly clear to most Christians who have read it throughout the history of the church. Understanding the passage as history stretches back to the time of the apostles and the writing of the New Testament. Consequently, since it is clear, it carries with it the authority of the Word of God. To claim otherwise is to either deny perspicuity (the Bible is obscure and requires special interpretation only by experts) or inspiration (Genesis 1-11 is not the authoritative Word of God). I do not accept either of those conclusions. Genesis 1-11 is best understood as a series of historical accounts that are rich with theological meaning.

These three witnesses—text, tradition, and theology—agree together that the first eleven chapters of Genesis describe the history of creation. There was a sudden creation, a fall, a flood, and a confusion at Babel. That is not to say that Genesis is a history textbook or a science book. This is yet another annoying caricature perpetuated by theistic evolutionists. Creationists do not abuse the Bible by recognizing the history it communicates. We fully affirm the theology and theological importance of Genesis, but we also recognize that none of the theology is negated by the historical details communicated. Instead, we affirm with the apostle Paul that "these things happened to them as an example, but they were written down for our instruction" (I Corinthians 10:11).

Genesis records for us the outline of events that took place during the earliest periods of earth history, with an eye toward the theological importance of the events. Genesis is often uninterested in the kinds of scientific details I would like to know, but that does not mean that I can ignore the historical implications from what I read there. History goes hand in hand with theology.

ADOREMUS 5

The toughest, hardiest, most resilient of all God's animals is a tiny little "bear" called a tardigrade. More than a thousand species of these little water bears are known from every corner of the world, in the most unlikely of places. You could lay fifty tardigrades end to end in a single inch. Their plump little bodies have eight stubby legs with tiny tufts of claws on each foot. They eat by stabbing their food with their mouth stylets and sucking up the juicy contents.

But the most striking thing about the tardigrade is its endurance. Explorers found tardigrades under solid ice caps and in the boiling water of hot springs. They live on the tops of the highest mountains and the depths of the deepest ocean. They're found from pole to pole even in average environments like ponds or lakes or streams.

To endure these crazy environments, tardigrades can "suspend their metabolism." They basically shut down their bodies and their cells. They can survive thirty years with no food or water, then rehydrate and go about their little water bear business. They can tolerate six thousand times the pressure we experience in the earth's air at sea level. Some tardigrades can withstand temperatures hundreds of degrees above and below zero. Others can survive radiation that would fry any other animal. Some survived even the vacuum of outer space, confirmed by an actual space mission where water bears were shot into orbit for ten days. Two thirds of the little guys survived. They didn't live very long after returning to earth (space was not good for them), but they did better than we ever could.[36]

As we marvel at these durable little bears, we remember that the God who made them tough is a God of unspeakable strength and power. He made these water bears. He made their environments. He made the heat of fire and the cold of ice. He made the radiation of space and the pressure of the ocean. He made it all.

The Bible speaks often and loudly of the strength of God. He is the strength of Israel, the power of Samson, our fortress of refuge. He gives strength to the weak and authority to the king. He is our strong tower, our rock and fortress and deliverer. Who is this king of glory? The Lord strong and mighty, the Lord mighty in battle. The God who gave endurance to the tardigrade gives grace to you and me.

> *God is our refuge and strength,*
> *a very present help in trouble.*
> *Therefore we will not fear though the earth gives way,*
> *though the mountains be moved into the heart of the sea,*
> *though its waters roar and foam,*
> *though the mountains tremble at its swelling.*
> *(Psalm 43:1-3)*

6
SIGNPOSTS
OF SCIENCE

But what about the science!? You can't just **ignore** all the overwhelming evidence that the earth and universe are billions of years old and life evolved by natural processes. You're an idiot!

I've heard statements like that plenty of times from Christians and non-Christians alike. It's usually accompanied by widened eyes, red faces, and occasional flecks of airborne spittle. My favorite email I ever received was a one-liner that said, "you are teh stupidest person in the world," which sort of undercut its own credibility with the misspelling. Sometimes I laugh at the reactions I get, and sometimes they're frustrating. I'd really like to have thoughtful conversations and maybe even learn new things, but more often, emotions just take over and shut everything down.

So let's just address this right now: Am I against science or maybe even a pseudoscientist? I don't think so. I don't know how I could be anti-science having studied science for years, worked as a scientist, attended scientific conferences and meetings in the United States and Europe, and derived an immense amount of pleasure from doing so. As for pseudoscience, I'm not sure what that even means. I usually see it used for things that look like science but disagree with the mainstream. I'm not sure I want to use the term *pseudoscience*, because it mostly just strikes me as name calling. If something's bad science or bad scholarship, I think we can just call it *bad* without making up fancy words just to put people down.

Do I ignore all of science, as many critics contend? Well, to some extent, yes, I do. After all, I'm trained only as a biochemist. I have some skill in the field of evolutionary biology and something called comparative genomics, but beyond that, I'm kind of a novice. When it comes to the age of the universe or radiometric dating or the fossil record, I must, as a matter of practical convenience, ignore much of it. I can't, as one person, re-invent *all* of science. It's just preposterous to expect otherwise.

What about the science that I do know? I confess I have a greater responsibility here. How can I claim to understand evolutionary biology and yet still hold onto young-age creationism? I've been answering this question in the previous chapters, as I've outlined my thoughts on the Bible and my faith. I know from my own experience that God is real and speaks through the pages of scripture. I am convinced by my study of scripture that it records true historical facts about the world. That's where my thoughts about creation begin, with my own experience with the creator.

What to Do with Science

So what do I do with the science? Let's think through the problem first. I have no doubt that evidence from creation can be interpreted as a multi-billion-year history of the world and the gradual evolution of all living things from a common ancestor. This includes evidence totally unknown in Darwin's day, like the similarity of DNA and proteins from different species, radiometric dating, and fossils of intermediate creatures. Add to that the fact that these disparate lines of evidence appear to converge on the same explanation. This convergence is called consilience, and it's a separate piece of evidence all by itself. Even if I could say that protein similarity doesn't really support evolution or radiometric dating has some problems, that wouldn't necessarily defeat evolution because the consilience of all the other evidences is still there. In my experience, consilience is probably the number one reason that people accept evolution. It's just hard to imagine how so many different sorts of evidence could all point to the same *wrong* conclusion.

This is a really important point, too. I see a lot of creationists spending a lot of time, energy, and money proving this or that part of evolution is wrong. And yet, here we are. Evolutionary theory continues to grow and spread in power and influence. People are unconvinced by these efforts. Not all people, of course. There are some who find these refutations very compelling, but many more just think back to that consilience issue. It's really hard to imagine how a conclusion with so many different pieces of evidence could be so completely wrong.

Consilient models require consilient replacements. And those replacement models must be better than the old one, or people will never let go of the old one. In the case of evolution, we can't just be satisfied saying, "It's wrong." Creationists have to pony up. We have to explain what these evidences really mean and how they fit into a consilient picture of creation. That's what I call model building, and model building is the heart of the quest.

How does one build a model? First of all, it requires knowledge of the science, and this knowledge isn't gained by reading Wikipedia or the latest evolution book. Understanding science takes sustained, practical, first-hand study, and it needs to be guided by an expert. If you're really serious about understanding God's creation, that understanding really does take a Ph.D. It's true that there are exceptions, and having a Ph.D. doesn't guarantee you'll be competent at science. But the average Ph.D. scientist understands their field far, far better than a guy who read a book about it.

Not just any Ph.D. will do either. Creationism needs trained scientists in relevant fields. If you want to study fossils, you need a paleontology degree. If you want to study the origin of species, get an evolutionary biology degree. Don't settle for medical studies or engineering. Just having a degree doesn't make you an expert in everything.

That really shouldn't come as a surprise to anyone. Science is no different than literally any other human activity. People don't learn to drive or cook or play football just by reading books. Think about it: Would you trust your surgeon if he'd only ever read about surgery? Then why would you trust the scientific opinions of people who've only read about science? We should value science education guided by established and competent scientists because we value every other form of education guided by experts.

With a good scientific training in hand, how do we construct a new model that's better than the old one? I have five suggestions that can put us on the right track:

1. **Think weird.** A good scientist should be quick to evaluate ideas and prioritize the ones that are most likely to be worthwhile. Unfortunately, since we're all trained in the conventional paradigm of evolution, we need to think more creatively than we're prone to do. We need to be willing to entertain and explore even the strangest ideas, as long as they're not obviously wrong and a waste of time.

2. **Think carefully.** There may be parts of the conventional model that could be useful in the creation model. Not everything about evolution is necessarily wrong. Keep the good, and throw out the bad.

3. **Examine anomalies.** Is there anything the conventional model explains poorly? Are there any errors or problems that crop up in conventional explanations? These are the sorts of things creationists get very excited about, but their real value is not falsifying conventional science. Anomalies are clues to the correct model. We need to examine them very carefully.

4. **Don't take anybody's word for it.** Is there something completely settled in conventional science? Something that *everyone knows* is true? Look at it again. Repeat the research and try to confirm it. This has been an amazingly fruitful avenue of research for creationists.

5. **Think of creative ways to evaluate creationist claims.** There is a rich depth and history to creationist literature, even though not all of it is worth reading. We need to be acquainted with this tradition to avoid re-inventing the wheel and to help refine old ideas and move the field forward.

These suggestions aren't a recipe for success. They won't guarantee a new, compelling model if we follow them. They're only a start. They're guides for the quest, but the quest will take time. Certainly more than one lifetime. But the end is worth it, for the end is God. Understanding God's creation is understanding God.

These suggestions also summarize a lot of the most successful creationist research that I've observed, and in that way, they loudly affirm that creationism *is* science. Far too often, science is understood as nothing more than knowledge. In fact, the original Latin word for knowledge, *scientia*, is the origin of our English word *science*. This is reinforced by too many tedious science classes that focus on memorizing trivia.

The real core of science isn't knowledge though. It's discovery. Science is a method of explaining the world around us by carefully controlled observations. Science is an activity, and it's always growing, revising, and changing. Sometimes creationists snicker at science for not producing certain knowledge. We see headlines all the time about discoveries that call into question all sorts of accepted ideas in science, but that's good. That's what science should be doing. No one's understanding of creation is perfect. Scientists should always be learning new things, making new discoveries, and revising past errors.

Science is also deeply pragmatic. Ideas that are testable, that make predictions and explain data are what scientists will work with, even if the scientists themselves are skeptical of the ideas and are only out to disprove them. The process of science can still apply, and if that works, if you can test an idea with science, then it must have been a scientific hypothesis in the first place. Even if it's wrong.

At the beginning of this chapter, I said I didn't really like the term *pseudoscience*. Personally, it just seems like an insult, but practically, it doesn't really represent what's happening in science. If you can find a way to evaluate your idea using science, even if it's a terrible idea, then it has entered the world of science.

Creationism is science, or at least it can be. We may not yet have all the answers to the kinds of questions scientists want to know, but we have begun the process of studying creation and developing our alternative model.

Still don't believe me? Let's look at some examples.

Footprints in the Coconino

The Coconino is a layer of light-colored sandstone near the top of the rock layers exposed in the Grand Canyon. The light color makes it really recognizable, even from space. The sandstone extends across Nevada, Arizona, Utah, and Colorado. It's well-known as a "cross-bedded" sandstone. Cross-beds are layers that run at an angle to the actual layer of the sandstone. Cross-bedded sandstone looks like it has diagonal stripes running through it.

This cross-bedding is one of the reasons geologists believe that the Coconino was formed from desert sand dunes. Cross-bedding happens when sand piles up with one angled side. In the wind, new sand blows over the top of the dune and tumbles down the side. Cross-bedding is the angled surface of ancient sand dunes. We can test this in the modern world by examining sand dunes that exist today and confirming that they also have cross-beds.

The Coconino is also known for its fossils, especially its fossil footprints. The footprints I want to talk about are the tracks of some kind of reptile or amphibian. The tracks are well-preserved. They're small and about as wide as they are long, less than an inch overall. Four toes are visible in many of the tracks, and so is the pile of sand kicked up behind the heel.

What would a creationist think about the formation of the Coconino Sandstone? Most young-age creationists today accept flood geology, the idea that the global flood in the time of Noah is responsible for a large part of the fossil record. This Coconino Sandstone is a Permian sandstone, which means that it's right in the middle of what most creationists believe was formed by the flood. So how could a desert sandstone form in the middle of a flood when the surface of the world was under water?

Researcher Leonard Brand examined these trackways firsthand in the Coconino Sandstone. He counted the number of tracks at his study sites, then recorded the number of footprints that preserved toe marks and the number that preserved heel marks. He found that slightly more than 80% of the tracks preserved toe marks and slightly more than 70% preserved marks from the soles of the feet.

Brand observed two other weird feature of the trackways. First, the toes often pointed in the same direction but not the direction the animal was traveling. It was like the animal was doing a sidestep along the dune. Even weirder, some trackways would abruptly stop and then appear again several feet away. Could these animals fly?

Brand went back to his lab and created an artificial sand dune (also called a pile of sand) and put an orange-bellied newt on it to observe what kind of tracks it would make. Running on completely dry sand, the newt left very few toe tracks but a lot of sole marks. That should sound familiar to anyone who's ever walked across a dry, sandy beach. Toe marks don't last in dry sand. The sand caves in on top of them.

When the newts ran across wet sand, their toe marks were preserved very well. Every track had toe marks, but fewer than 40% preserved the mark of the sole. Neither dry sand nor wet sand seemed to be a very good match to the footprints from the Coconino.

Brand also ran the newts across the surface of sand that he piled up under water. Those trackways preserved both toe marks and sole marks. A bit less than 90% of the tracks preserved toe marks, and almost 70% preserved sole marks. Tracks made underwater were the closest match to the characteristics of the fossil footprints of the Coconino Sandstone. You could even imagine an animal trying to walk while being pushed along by a water current, so the toes don't face the direction the animal is moving, and occasionally the animal is caught up in the current and dropped down again a few feet away.[37]

This is one of those great examples of re-examining something everyone just knows is true. The Coconino is a textbook example of an ancient desert sand dune. In fact, Permian sandstones are known from around the world, and geologists think they're mostly ancient sand dunes. Much to everyone's surprise, though, Brand's research provided one piece of evidence that the Coconino was actually formed underwater.

Fossil Hominins

In chapter two, I described my own research with fossil hominins, the creatures in the fossil record that appear to be most similar to human beings (and some of them are human beings). As I explained there, fossil digs from the past fifty years have remarkably expanded our understanding of humans and the animals that most closely resemble us. I can definitely imagine how an evolutionist might see these discoveries as confirmation of human evolution.

My work in baraminology is an ongoing attempt to test the creationist claim that humans and apes are distinct. I already talked about my frustration with *Australopithecus sediba* and its consistent clustering with other creatures I took to be human. What I didn't emphasize is the fact that there were still clusters. In other words, we could still draw a line between creatures I took to be human, like Neandertals, and creatures that were almost certainly animals, like the Lucy skeleton (*Australopithecus afarensis*). Even though the human group is a bit bigger than I expected, this is still a pretty exciting result. After all, with all the fossil hominins we now know about, you might expect an unbroken chain from animals like Lucy to modern human beings, but that's not the case. Instead, we find discrete groups that do not overlap. The creationist prediction seems to be confirmed in this case. I've done several additional studies with fossils that have been discovered since *sediba*, and I keep finding the same result. Humans are humans, apes are apes, and they don't overlap.[38]

Moving forward on the Quest

What should we make of these research results? Do they *prove* that creation is true after all? No, they don't. Not at all. They raise many more questions than they answer. In his footprint research, Brand didn't look at the cross-bedding of the Coconino, one of the classic evidences of a wind-blown sand dune. How could creationists explain that? Even if we could show conclusively that the Coconino formed under water, how would that prove the flood? There are many rock layers that are believed to have formed under water, just like there are other rock layers that are believed to have formed on dry land. There is much research still to do to fully understand the formation of the fossil record. Brand's work is just one step.

There are questions about the hominins as well. The biggest one is the genetic evidence. Studies of the human and chimpanzee genomes since the early seventies have consistently shown a remarkable similarity between the two.[39] Even if there's a gap in the fossil record detected by baraminology, how can we explain the genomic similarity? Baraminology studies are also vulnerable to future research. What happens with the next fossil discovery? Will it also fall in the existing human or ape groups, or will it do something altogether different? Hominin baraminology is just a start.

Clearly, there is still much research to be done, but that should not diminish the success of these research projects. For me, successful projects like these act as road signs. Back in the days before satellite navigation was common, I used to navigate by studying a paper road map. While driving, I had to depend on road signs to confirm that I was on the right track. Whenever I saw the sign I was looking for, I knew I was going the right way.

So too with creationist research. As I navigate the challenging road of building a new paradigm, I rely on these small successes to remind me that I'm on the right road. These successes are like God encouraging me to keep going and not give up. The quest to replace conventional science with a new model perhaps isn't so crazy after all. I find in these small victories a reminder that this quest is actually going somewhere.

This encouragement is called hope. This isn't hope in the sense of wishing for something, but hope in the biblical sense of faith that looks forward. Let's face it, the quest for God often begins with the absurd. God tells an old man that his wife will have a baby. God calls a murderer in hiding to free his people from slavery. God tells His army to conquer a city by marching around it in silence. What sense does any of this make? None, except that God's foolishness far surpasses any human attempts at wisdom.

But where God calls, he also gives faith and hope to those who ask. Faith comes by hearing the Word of God, as I study to know him better and to understand what he revealed about his creation. Hope comes from putting that faith to the test. Will God's promises really work in the real world? Can I test things like the Coconino Sandstone or the Neandertals and make sense of what God has said? Hope grows with success.

There is nothing new about this evolution business. The God who called Elijah and Jeremiah to stand against culture and kingdom is still God today. The God who calls us again and again to believe the impossible is the God who parts the Red Sea, brings water to the desert, and raises the dead. God's in the business of doing the impossible. He gives faith, and he gives hope.

ADOREMUS 6

In my experience, ravens are just about as common as dirt. Everywhere I travel, those squawky birds aren't far behind. About forty different species inhabit our planet, going by other names like rook, jackdaw, and crow. They're found on every continent that isn't Antarctica, often in huge numbers. They can roost in groups of more than a thousand at a time and deafen the ear with their KAW KAW KAW! A typical raven will probably live twenty years. In captivity, they might reach thirty or forty. They mate for life, and they'll eat just about anything, food or not.

Crows also possess an immense intelligence. In Israel, the local crows have figured out how to use bread as fish bait. In the islands of New Caledonia, crows carefully select twigs to bend into hooks for snatching food, like grubs or small lizards. Those same crows can teach their children how to do the same tricks.

In one study, researchers taught ravens how to use a little machine to get food by activating it with a small tool. They also provided the ravens with "distractor" tools that would not open the machine and free the food. The next day, a full seventeen hours later, the ravens remembered how to use the tool to open the machine in 90% of the experiments. In the same research study, almost all ravens remembered a simple bartering system, where they could trade a specific token to a human being for food.[40]

Crows also remember faces. In Seattle, researchers wore face masks to capture, tag, and release a set of wild crows. The same researchers then asked people of different sizes, ages, and genders to wear the masks around the crows. Not surprisingly, the crows mobbed and squawked at them.[41]

Crows remember, and so does their creator.

The Bible describes over and over God's attention to his creatures. In the midst of the greatest disaster the world has ever seen, God remembered Noah. When he rained down judgment on Sodom and Gomorrah, God remembered Abraham and saved Lot. When Rachel and Hannah could not conceive, God remembered them and gave them baby boys. When the Israelites suffered in slavery to Egypt, God remembered them and sent a deliverer. In the midst of the turmoil and pain of this fallen world, God remembers his promises to us. He remembers his mercy and his love. He remembers us.

Just like the raven, just like us, God remembers.

He has remembered his steadfast love and faithfulness
to the house of Israel.
All the ends of the earth have seen
the salvation of our God.
(Psalm 98:3)

7
QUESTIONS FROM GENESIS

The great danger on any quest is becoming complacent where you are, especially when those on the quest with you already agree with you closely on many things. And let's face it, people regularly self-segregate according to cultural factors and beliefs. As we ponder the mysteries of God's creation, we can easily get locked into certain erroneous ways of thinking, and like-minded friends probably won't recognize the error, since they think the same way. These hang-ups can hinder our ability to move forward on the quest.

This tendency to get stuck on mistaken ideas is why we must always be willing to re-examine our understanding of the Bible as well as science. I mentioned in chapter five that there are open questions in scripture, but I didn't really explore them. Here, I want to revisit those questions. We cannot simply approach the quest as if the only problems are scientific and the Bible is already fully understood. It's arrogant to assume you understand everything about the Bible. We run the risk of getting caught in simple error when we neglect the scripture. We might end up believing things not for good reason but because we "just know" that they're true.

Maggots and Kinds

Consider spontaneous generation. Most of us are taught somewhere in our schooling that people used to believe that flies, worms, and "lower" creatures were generated directly from the earth or from decaying bodies. At the end of the seventeenth century, Francesco Redi performed his famous experiments that showed that maggots were not generated from rotting meat but from female flies laying their eggs on rotting meat. Redi's experiments reversed centuries of belief about the origin of creatures and ushered in a whole new way of thinking about God's creation.

Prior to Redi, not only did people believe in spontaneous generation, but it also showed up repeatedly in interpretations of Genesis. Basil of Caesarea, a fourth century bishop in Asia Minor, wrote,

> "Let the earth bring forth the living creature." This command has continued and earth does not cease to obey the Creator. For, if there are creatures which are successively produced by their predecessors, there are others that even today we see born from the earth itself (*Hexameron* IX:2)

We see here that spontaneous generation was not seen as some kind of random, godless origin of life but as a divinely-instituted power of the earth itself. God created the earth so that it could bring forth the lower creatures. This interpretation is found commonly in Christian commentaries on Genesis through the ages all the way to the seventeenth century.

And now we know it was a mistake. It wasn't a terrible mistake, and it didn't cause any heresy. Belief in spontaneous generation probably slowed down the progress of science more than eroding anyone's spiritual health, but that's still a hindrance to our quest to understand God's creation. And it's a good reminder to always search the scriptures to make sure you really understand what they say.

In my own work, I've discovered a bunch of misconceptions that I needed to abandon. The one that sticks most closely with me is the very common claim that God made animals to reproduce after their kinds. The earliest I can find this claim is in Herbert W. Morris's 1871 *Science and the Bible*:

> God made each living creature, it is said, *after his kind*. By this phrase we are to understand, not only that God

contrived and created the different species of animals in all their variety of forms, instincts, and habits; but also, that He so made them, as to produce each its own kind, and its kind only, through all its successive generations. It is in virtue of this law, a law established throughout the animal kingdom, that the several races of animals have been kept distinct from the foundation of the world to the present day.[42]

We continue to hear such claims commonly in creationism today. Some even claim that this law of kinds is clearly taught in Genesis. Because I had heard and read it in so many places, it didn't occur to me to actually consult Genesis on this subject until I actually wanted to write about this law myself. That's when I realized that it wasn't in Genesis. The Bible teaches no such law.

Don't believe me? That's okay. Look for yourself. Don't take my word for it. Here are the two passages where God creates animals:

> So God created the great sea creatures and every living creature that moves, with which the waters swarm, according to their kinds, and every winged bird according to its kind. And God saw that it was good. And God blessed them, saying, "Be fruitful and multiply and fill the waters in the seas, and let birds multiply on the earth." And God made the beasts of the earth according to their kinds and the livestock according to their kinds, and everything that creeps on the ground according to its kind. And God saw that it was good. (Genesis 1:21-22, 25)

Notice the phrase "according to its kind" describes either the animals created or the act of creation. It's not clear. The command to be fruitful and multiply follows the creation of flying and swimming things, but that command (to reproduce) doesn't say anything about kinds. Whatever it means, "after its kind" acts like a contrast to the "image of God" when God creates human beings. Where animals were created after their kinds, humans were made in God's image, as his representatives.

That doesn't mean that everything we think about created kinds is wrong. That doesn't mean that kinds can change into other kinds or that they can crossbreed and make new kinds. It does mean that those questions have to be studied and answered without using Herbert Morris's argument. Morris was wrong.

More Questions

There are other parts in our understanding of Genesis that are potentially more important. I want to emphasize one more time that I am settled in my commitment to young-age creationism, but just like all relationship commitments, making a commitment doesn't mean I understand everything I'm getting into. I have also noticed that recent critics of creationism have really turned up the pressure on certain points that I'll mention below.

First, I'm really curious about the way the various narratives of Genesis all fit together. The earliest narratives are pretty sporadic until you get to the family of Abraham. If you follow Ussher's chronology, Genesis 1-11 covers about 2,000 years of history, but Genesis 12-50 covers only about 300 years. Obviously, we have to consider the thematic differences here, since Abraham is the father of the Israelites, and the story ought to focus on him. Nevertheless, it does make me wonder where those earlier stories came from. Were they records that were written down somehow and later compiled? Were they stories that were handed down orally? Or were they simply visions given to the author to record?

This question is becoming more and more important as an increasing majority of evangelical scholars have accepted modern views on the authorship of the Pentateuch. Instead of seeing it as a product largely of Moses, as the New Testament and Christian tradition does, many (most?) young, evangelical Old Testament scholars believe it was compiled from earlier fragments that were heavily edited and re-written after the Jews returned from the exile. The formation of Genesis 1-11 and its relationship to the pagan mythology the Jews encountered in Babylon have been emphasized by theistic evolutionists trying to explain why Genesis 1-11 isn't really historical. There have been some really good responses to this new trend in Genesis scholarship, but I still wonder about some of the elements of Genesis 1-11 that lead scholars to adopt these post-exilic theories.[43] I think there is much more to be said on this subject.

I also wonder about the relationship of Genesis 1 and 2. These two chapters present two views of the creation of humans. In the first, cosmic creation culminates with the creation of humanity in God's image as rulers of the world. In the second, human creation is an intimate act of sculpting and breathing, and God intends for humans to serve creation in the Garden of Eden. Tradition tells us that Genesis 2 elaborates on the events of the sixth day of creation described in Genesis 1, but this does not clear up all questions.

Particularly puzzling is the order of creation. In Genesis 1, the order of events takes a prominent position in the narrative, and humans appear to be created after everything else. Theirs is the final act of creation. In contrast, Genesis 2 appears to the casual reader as if humans are created first, even before the plants. Before Adam was created, there were no plants of the field, and after God created Adam, God himself created the Garden of Eden. Then God decided it was not good for Adam to be alone, and the animals were made.

I think most of these difficulties can be easily cleared up by paying attention to what the text does and does not say in chapter two. The plants described as being absent at the time of creation are plants "of the field," and their absence is attributed to the lack of a farmer. This sounds more like the origin of agriculture than the origin of all plants. Remember not to read into the text what isn't there.

The animals, however, are a bit more puzzling. God definitely makes the birds one day before making humans and the land animals in Genesis 1, but in Genesis 2, the narrative seems to require that God made the birds and animals together in response to Adam's solitude.

> Then the Lord God said, "It is not good that the man should be alone; I will make him a helper fit for him." Now out of the ground the Lord God had formed every beast of the field and every bird of the heavens and brought them to the man to see what he would call them. (Genesis 2:18-19)

Notice here, the English Standard Version says that God "had formed" the birds and animals, as if this was something that already happened. That is a possible reading of the text, but it's also possible to read it as if the creation took place after God's statement about man being alone, which is the more common translation. Translating the verb as "had formed" is one way to clear up the apparent discrepancy.[44] There have been other suggestions as well. It's an interesting puzzle.

This is yet another issue that is frequently raised by critics of creationism. They exaggerate the differences and claim that Genesis 1 and 2 are flatly contradictory on numerous points.[45] So even if we wanted to take these chapters "literally," we can't because they don't make sense. The meaning of Genesis 1 and 2 supposedly must lie elsewhere. As I said, I think this is an exaggeration. Points of contradiction are read *into* the text rather than read *from* the text. I think the traditional understanding of Genesis 2 as an expansion of the events of day six is still a very plausible explanation of the differences, but it definitely needs further study.

Another big issue that I've mentioned already is the question of animal death. This is a standard and important concept in young-age creationism, but it is extremely underdeveloped. As the argument goes, the death curse on creation as a result of Adam's sin applied to humans and to animals. Thus, animals before the fall were physically immortal just like people were. The key result of this is that the fossil record, which is full of dead animals, must have formed after the fall. This rules out old-age creationism and all forms of theistic evolution.

The difficulty is that the Bible never plainly says that animals didn't die before the fall. I think there are plenty of hints to that effect, but it's not spelled out. For example, the animals are given plants for food when they are created (Genesis 1:30), and the serpent is cursed above the other animals (Genesis 3:14), implying that other animals were also cursed. When God sent the flood to punish sin, the text says that "all flesh" had become corrupt, animals included (Genesis 6:11-13). Isaiah indicates that the coming kingdom of God will include peace between predator and prey (Isaiah 11:6-9), and all creation groans in anticipation of the coming kingdom (Romans 8:22-23). When you put all these passages together, you get the sense that animals were different before the fall. The curse was more than just human punishment. The curse impacted the entire creation. In theological terms, it was a "cosmic curse."

The concept of animal immortality raises a host of hard questions. First of all, how would this sinless and deathless creation not be overrun with vermin? Death plays an important role today in regulating population size. In our fallen creation, death is unquestionably necessary and good. If animals never died, how did their populations not just explode? Second, which animals were immortal? All animals? Some animals? Creationists have disagreed on this point. Some have argued that all animal death is post-fall.[46] Others allow that "lower" animals, such as insects, fish, or even lizards, could have died before the fall.[47] Third, how are some animals so well designed for hunting and killing if there was no death before the fall? This is an ongoing area of creationist thought and research.

Naturally, theistic evolutionists want to include animal death in the goodness of creation, and some even want to allow for human death before the fall.[48] They point to the ambiguities of the text and the hard questions raised by animal immortality to support their claims. They sound plausible doing so, and this is yet another reason creationists need to articulate very clearly a well-reasoned and well-supported position on animal death and the fall. This position should not be just a refutation of theistic evolution that ignores the difficulties of immortal animals. Rather, we need an excellent position on animal death that is uniquely creationist and addresses the hard questions.

Be a Berean

There are plenty of other questions that I could mention, but the key is not so much which question to ask. The key is the willingness to study the scripture. On his second missionary journey, his first time preaching the gospel in Europe, the apostle Paul visited the town of Berea, where Luke recorded that the Jews in the Synagogue "were more noble than those in Thessalonica; they received the word with all eagerness, examining the scriptures daily to see if these things were so" (Acts 17:11). These Berean Jews didn't just take Paul's word for it. They checked his claims out for themselves, and as a result, "Many of them therefore believed" (Acts 17:12).

We too should check things out for ourselves. After all, if our understanding of the Bible is right, then there is no harm in checking again, but if we've made a mistake, we need to know. That means a willingness to question and re-examine everything we think we know, including the biggest and most sacred doctrines of creationism: the age of creation, death and the fall, and the global flood. Remember that this isn't merely a matter of doubt or even refuting others' doubts. This is about understanding God's creation and a willingness to search for his truth. We can be assured that the Holy Spirit will affirm what is true and correct what is wrong.

ADOREMUS 7

All living things have bodies made of trillions and trillions of cells, little sacks of chemicals that gather energy from the environment and put it to work. Within each cell, tiny bundles of atoms catalyze all those energy transactions and chemical transformations that cells need to do. We call those bundles of atoms enzymes. There are thousands of different enzymes in most cells, and most are extremely tiny. Imagine a cell the size of the Empire State Building, and the average enzyme would still be smaller than a ping pong ball. Tiny they may be, but their influence extends far beyond any one cell. The most important and common of all enzymes is a flattened, disk-shaped blob from the leaves of green plants. Scientists call it ribulose-1,5-carboxylase/oxygenase, but scientists who prefer not to trip over tongue-twisters call it rubisco.

Rubisco grabs carbon dioxide out of the atmosphere and attaches it to sugar in a reaction driven by the energy of the sun. In short, rubisco makes plants grow, and as they grow, those rubisco-made sugars are eaten by animals, which are eaten by other animals. As animals burn those plant sugars, they get energy to do their animal things. After all those plant sugars are burned and the energy is used, the only thing left is carbon dioxide, which starts the whole cycle over again. Rubisco, that insignificant blob you can't even see, makes life on this planet, in these bodies, possible.

When the apostle Paul wrote to the Corinthians feuding over their spiritual gifts, Paul compared the church to a body. Feuding in the church makes about as much sense as feuding among the parts of the body. Everyone wants to be front and center in the church, showing off and getting those ego-boosting accolades. But just like a body needs more than just a face or a hand, so too the Body of Christ needs its unseen and unsung members. "As it is, God arranged the members in the body, each one of them, as he chose. If all were a single member, where would the body be? As it is, there are many parts, yet one body" (I Corinthians 12:18-20).

As we look back at these words two thousand years later, with all our knowledge of creatures and cells and enzymes, we see with new eyes how right Paul was. Just like our bodies, our entire world is full of tiny blobs that maintain the life of the entire planet. But just like the Corinthians, we still struggle with our place in the body of Christ, mistaking fame for importance in the eyes of God. The God who made unseen rubisco is the God who saves us. The God who designed this world to run on a tiny, solar-powered enzyme is the good shepherd who left the ninety-nine to come find that one lost sheep.

There is no one insignificant in the body of Christ.

8
THE HARDEST
QUESTIONS

I was talking to a friend recently about how overwhelmed I sometimes feel running the creationist ministry Core Academy of Science. I never had a business class in my life, and running a business of my own is challenging, to say the least. He suggested that I read a book by Peter Thiel called *Zero to One*. Thiel is a tech billionaire entrepreneur and co-founder of Paypal, and his book summarized some thoughts on technology business that Thiel presented in a course at Stanford University. The book was full of a lot of interesting advice about businesses, some of which was already familiar and some was helpful and new.

What really grabbed my attention, though, was Thiel's comments on the Unabomber, Ted Kaczynski. At the time, all I knew about the Unabomber was that he had used bombs to terrorize people and that he wrote a manifesto. Thiel was intrigued by the manifesto, in which Kaczynski explained his motivation. He recognized the three categories of problems commonly recognized by engineers: easy, hard, and impossible. Easy problems are trivial, and impossible problems can't be solved. Hard problems, though, require discipline and effort, and their solutions are the stuff of legend. According to Kaczynski, solving hard problems is the only source of human satisfaction, and he believed that technology had solved all the hard problems, which made human existence unsatisfying. So he wanted to bomb us back to the dark ages.

Thiel was intrigued by the connection between solving hard questions and satisfaction. As he explained hard questions, he wrote,

> Religious fundamentalism, for example, allows no middle ground for hard questions: there are easy truths that children are expected to rattle off, and then there are the mysteries of God, which can't be explained. In between—the zone of hard truths—lies heresy.[49]

I remember very clearly reading that for the first time when one of those eureka moments hit me. This formulation of easy/hard/impossible questions encapsulated my own journey in creationism. I refuse to settle for easy answers that do not resolve outstanding questions. I always push the limit of what we know, and when I do, I try the patience of those convinced that we have all the answers we need. In short, the sometimes fiery reactions to my work can be traced, in part, to this zone of hard truths, where heresy lies. My work has never actually been heretical, but hard questions always run that risk.

What are these hard questions, then? And why aren't current creationist ideas adequate to address them? There are actually many hard questions, and I've already mentioned quite a few in previous chapters. Listing them all would be an "impossible problem!" In this chapter, I want to call attention to four basic challenges in four major fields of study: astronomy, geology, biology, and anthropology. Once again, as I have emphasized repeatedly in this book, I'm not trying to highlight questions to degrade or denigrate creationists or creationism. My goal, as it always has been, is to increase our understanding of creation. My goal is the quest, and things that weigh us down and prevent us from making progress need to be left behind so we can focus on the road ahead.

Most importantly, we must stop accusing people of heresy over every little disagreement we have. Yes, I know that actual heresy is a pretty rare claim for creationists, but I have personally been accused of being an evolutionist, of being brainwashed by the enemy, and leading people away from the gospel of Jesus Christ. I've seen colleagues accused of compromising with the enemy and many other insulting insinuations.

I've even made these sorts of accusations. I remember vividly being rebuked by a kind friend when I called someone I disagreed with a "false teacher." He was right to rebuke me. There's a big difference between honest mistakes and false teaching. There's also a big difference between honest disagreement and false teaching. And teaching erroneous science isn't remotely the same as teaching a false gospel. Somewhere in this world of disagreement, we need to make room for hard questions, for honest discussion, for the simple confession, "I don't know."

The Hardest Questions: Astronomy

I am not an astronomer, and I don't even try to keep up with the research and discoveries of astronomy. I only speak to this field as an outsider with concerns about how astronomy integrates with young-age creationism. In that regard, I think the hardest question in astronomy is how to explain the evidence of apparent history within a short chronology. To pose the question in its simplest form, how can we see stars that are farther away than 6,000 light years? This is the starlight problem.

The problem begins with a basic premise: Light has a speed in outer space: 186,000 miles per second, which is almost eight times around the earth in a single second. That's pretty fast, but space is also very big. The recent New Horizons mission to Pluto took ten years to get there, and it was traveling literally faster than a speeding bullet. So even though light moves, it still takes an appreciable amount of time to get from place to place.

The earth is about 93 million miles away from the sun on average, and when you do the math (93 million miles divided by 186,000 miles per second), you find out it takes about 8 minutes and 20 seconds for light to travel that far. Now here's where it gets really weird: Because you sense light by seeing it, when you look up in the sky, you don't see the sun where it actually is. You see it where it *was* 8 minutes and 20 seconds ago, because it took that long for the light to travel from the sun to your eyes.

Now, let's transfer that to things that are really far away, like the nearest star Proxima Centauri, which is approximately 24,800,000,000,000 miles away. That's 24.8 trillion miles. At highway speed, it would take you a little more than 37.2 million years to drive there. Light goes a lot faster of course, but it still takes the light from Proxima Centauri 4.22 years to get to earth. Since 4.22 is a smaller number than 24.8 trillion miles, astronomers measure distances between stars in light years, the distance light travels in a year. Proxima Centauri is 4.22 light years from earth.

If light from Proxima Centauri takes 4.22 years to get to the earth, then what we see when we look up into the sky is not Proxima Centauri as it is but as it was 4.22 years ago. We won't know what Proxima Centauri looks like today until 4.22 years from now when the light it made today arrives at earth. Seems really weird, doesn't it? But that's what you get when you start talking about the gigantic scale of the universe. We're all really puny.

The same sort of reasoning extends to things no matter how far away they are. The farthest visible things in the universe are billions of light years away, which means that the light from those objects should take billions of years to get here. How can it be that we can see these things if the universe itself is only thousands of years old? Put another way, if the universe really is only thousands of years old, how can we see stars farther way than thousands of light years? There hasn't been enough time for that light to travel here.

Creationists have proposed a number of explanations for this, and for that I am very glad. Very few creationists want to pretend this isn't a problem. Some solutions rely on changes in the way time flows in different parts of the universe, an idea that comes from Einstein's conception of physics.[50] For example, we might conceive of time flowing faster out there than it does here. So the universe could have aged billions of years in only a few earth minutes.

Others suggest that the solution might be more philosophical. Perhaps it's merely a matter of our assumptions when we examine light, and if we tweak those assumptions slightly the problem goes away. Perhaps light travels infinitely fast when it travels to the earth but about half the speed of light as it travels away?[51] Others suggest that this problem exists because God wanted it to appear that way. God made the starlight in transit already.[52]

As far as I'm aware, there is currently no solution to this hard question that all creationists agree on. Many do not like the idea of God creating light in transit, which makes God sound like he's created a false history that never existed. Others have concerns about approaches based on modern physics. So we keep looking, and this hard question remains.

The Hardest Questions: Geology

I know a bit more about geology than I do astronomy because I'm interested in the fossil record. But this is also not a special area of expertise for me, and so I can only summarize things in very basic terms. The hardest question here I think relates to the hardest question of astronomy: Why is there a pattern to radiometric dating?

We all know that scientists are confident as they declare this or that fossil "millions of years" old. These dates arise from a series of studies using radioisotopes—forms of matter that are unstable and break down in a regular way. I'm not really interested in all the details of how that works, at least not for this hard question, and I confess that's a bit unusual. Most people I know think that the very fact that a date can be calculated using radiometric dating is challenge enough, but I don't think so. A single measurement is at best interesting or provocative, but what happens when you try to replicate that measurement?

Early studies in ancient DNA were plagued by this problem. People were quick to publish the results of ancient DNA extractions that implied that DNA could survive for "millions" of years. This was surprising to many scientists, but attention to these sorts of studies quickly faded when other scientists failed to repeat the experiments. Being able to check someone else's work and confirm their results is an important ingredient in scientific research. If your result can't be replicated, no matter how provocative it might be, it could always be considered an anomaly—just a random whatever that isn't worth explaining.

For me then the hard question is not whether you can date a rock with radiometric dating. The real question is what happens when you try it again. What happens when you date the same rock or rock layer multiple times? What happens when you date multiple rock layers from a single column, one on top of the other? Do you find that the lowest are the oldest and the highest are the youngest? What is the pattern we find in thousands of radiometric dates?

For most radiometric dating of the same sample, the multiple dates generally agree, but that's true only in the general sense. There are plenty of examples of samples where the dates did not agree, and sometimes those disagreements are rather large.[53] Now here is where creationists get really excited, because these conflicting dates seem to say that radiometric dating doesn't work. Right? After all if you measure the same rock and one measurement says it's a quarter *million* years old and the next measurement says it's half a *billion*, then clearly something is screwy.

But remember that replication isn't about perfect replication. Anomalies happen all the time. The question is always the general trend: Are the anomalies the rule or the exception? In this case, they seem to be the exception. Rocks dated with multiple methods yield dates that are very consistent. Similar results can be observed in the geologic column, which describes the various layers of rock around the world. The lowest rocks, which appear to have been laid down before others in the column, generally date older than the higher rocks, which appear to have been laid down later.[54]

What can creationists make of this? Unlike the starlight problem, there is a sort of consensus on this question: Radiometric dates may be relatively correct. In other words, radiometric dates can tell us which rocks are older and which rocks are younger, even if they don't tell us precisely how old they are. There are a few creationists who contest even that simple conclusion, but most creationists that I know well do not.[55]

Why there is a relative consistency to radiometric dating is another matter. Some suggest it could be nothing more than changes in the mantle as rocks are formed, but the most widely-known solution is accelerated decay.[56] According to this model, radioisotopes do not decay at a regular rate, but have sometimes decayed much faster than they do today. This makes things appear to be older than they are, and it would preserve the relative consistency. It could account for all of the data that the conventional model does.

There are still questions about this model that need to be answered, including, "Why didn't all that heat generated by accelerated decay melt our planet?" So we can't consider accelerated decay a finished solution, but I'm excited to see research progress on this hard question. I'm also deeply grateful for organizations like the Institute for Creation Research and the Creation Research Society for trying to address these questions with a coordinated research project. Bravo! Now keep going! The quest isn't finished yet.

The Hardest Questions: Biology

Now we're getting into my territory, and the hardest question I see in biology is the one that captured my attention as a graduate student way back in 1994. Why do we share such similarity across all living things? Why do I have a similar anatomy to a chimpanzee? Why do I have similar proteins to bacteria and even viruses?

Now I know that the answer to that question *seems* obvious. We're similar because we all have a common designer, right? Just like different works of art from the same artist have common features, so too the living designs of our great Creator have common features. That's no surprise. So what's the problem?

Again, just like with the radiometric dating, I don't see the hard question as just the occurrence of similarity. The hard question is the *pattern* of similarity. Just like with radiometric dating, I want to look at the big picture, the broad trends. The larger trends show us something that looks like a meaningful pattern. The evolutionist tells us that the pattern is an evolutionary tree. This is what Darwin concluded in *Origin of Species*, and it's one of his evidences for evolution.[57]

Even though creationists are quick to (rightly) recognize a common designer as an explanation for the fact of similarity, the pattern of similarity is not so easy. We could simply say that God made the pattern that way, to which the evolutionist might reply, "Why did God make it look like evolution?" Another possibility that I think is closer to the truth is that the pattern of similarity really doesn't look like an evolutionary tree at all. If that's the case, the evolutionist's question doesn't really apply, because God did *not* make the pattern look like evolution. Perhaps the evolutionist should be asking, "Why was it so easy to see only what we wanted to see?"

Even if the pattern were more complex than an evolutionary tree, though, we still don't have an explanation for why it exists in the first place. Some of the pattern, perhaps the fine details of the pattern, is probably the result of common ancestry because we think that creatures that belong to the same created kind retain a core set of characteristics (more or less) that they inherited from the original members of the created kind that God made. But then there's the pattern formed by the created kinds themselves, a pattern that includes created kinds that look sort of like "evolutionary intermediates," even though they're really separate created kinds.

To me, this is sort of the ultimate holy grail for biology: understanding God's original design for the pattern of created kinds should be able to do amazing things like

- Identifying the created kinds. Since a pattern is formed by created kinds, the pattern should immediately identify all the created kinds for us. The question is how many created kinds do we need to identify before we can start to figure out the pattern of created kinds, which will then tell us what the rest of the created kinds are.

- Predicting organismal form. I think that the "evolutionary tree" is a dim reflection of some true aspect of God's design. Otherwise, I'm not sure how evolutionists are able to predict the discovery of things like *Australopithecus sediba* (see chapter two), feathered dinosaurs, or whales with hind limbs. If creationists could fill out the bigger picture of the pattern of similarity and show how design explains it better, all of those alleged "evolutionary intermediates" would immediately become confirming evidences of creation.

- Help us understand God Himself. This is the most exciting prospect to me. Understanding creation is just a step to understanding God. Creation may declare the glory of God, but He possesses that glory.

There is very little agreement among creationists on this question of the pattern of similarity, mostly because creationists continue to attribute the pattern to a common designer. That's sort of saying that "God made it that way" is the best we can hope for. Maybe that's true, but I doubt it. God doesn't do things for no reason at all. God has a plan for my life, just as He has a plan for all of creation. I believe that with prayer and seeking godly guidance, I can discover and live His plan for my life, and I think the same is probably true for creation. Again, though, it will take sustained effort. Answers don't just pop up when you're not looking. Jesus told us to seek in order to find.

The Hardest Questions: Anthropology

The origin of human diversity is not a big topic in creationism. In creationist circles, archaeological questions typically focus on things that directly impact the age of the earth, like Egyptian chronology, or the historicity of other parts of the Bible, like the exodus or the conquest. Otherwise, I think most of us look at the Bible's description of Noah and family coming off the ark and splitting up at the tower of Babel as the basic explanation for everything. As Noah's descendants became more numerous and widespread, humans themselves began to diverge physically, developing the variety of skin colors and other features that distinguish human populations today. Our picture of the development of humanity is like a simple tree, with a trunk representing Noah and family, and branches that represent their children and descendants.

Recent work in the new field of ancient genomics has shown this picture is much too simplistic.[58] Hundreds of ancient human genomes have now been analyzed, and the results show that the past was as genetically complicated as humanity is today. When we look at the earliest human beings of Europe, we find people groups as different from each other as Europeans and Asians today. Humanity's past does not appear to be any simpler than it is today.

Furthermore, scientists have also found that populations mixed together regularly in the past. In other words, when two separate populations met, they would intermarry and have children. Fighting and war was not the only outcome. Even more, the populations that intermingled weren't always what we think of as "anatomically modern humans," that is, *Homo sapiens*. Sometimes our ancestors intermarried with human beings that are way more different from us than any population alive today. I have good evidence that my own ancestors intermarried with Neandertals, and those Neandertals passed their genes on to me today.[59] The indigenous peoples of Papua New Guinea possess genes that came from a mysterious human form called Denisovans.[60] They are known only from a few sparse fossil teeth and a finger bone, from which scientists acquired a sample of their genomes. They are cousins to Neandertals, but they are more different from *Homo sapiens* than any Neandertals or anyone still living today.

This history of humanity is challenging our naïve expectations from reading scripture, but remember that the Bible is concerned with the history of salvation, not necessarily of all humanity. We read its abbreviated account of the table of nations in Genesis 10, and we think that's the whole story. But ancient genomics show us that the table of nations was followed by an amazing history of population dispersal and transformation, as different forms and different populations of human beings intermarried and merged. That process then gave us the people groups we observe today.

What makes this a hard question? The evidence seems to be counter to my naïve reading of Genesis. The deeper you go in human history, the more diverse we become. Instead of neatly tracing back to Noah's family, our genetics seem to get more and more complicated the farther back you go.[61]

I personally suspect this is also happening within all created kinds. I think there was a period after the flood during which genetic diversification and diversification of form was accelerated within many created kinds. As that period of diversification subsided, newer forms stopped appearing, and some of the previous forms died out. The result is a modern world in which created kinds look very neat and small with little diversity, when in fact, the fossil record shows us much greater diversity once existed. Now, genomes obtained from ancient human remains also show us the same pattern.

I wish I could say that my personal view was widely accepted, but it is completely rejected by some creationists. More than acceptance though, I wish that I had a better understanding of the history of humanity and the nature of genetic diversification so that my speculations were more explanatory and more compelling.

And even more than that, I wish somebody had a really compelling model for the history of humanity that could capture the consensus of creationists. I believe that day is coming though.

These are just a few of the hardest questions in creation. They're probably not even the hardest questions, but they are common and prominent and worthy of our attention. Regardless, this is where the quest moves forward. We don't succeed by being content with where we are but by pushing forward to the next horizon. The hardest questions are the next horizon. As God leads us, there is no reason to suspect that He will not bless our efforts.

ADOREMUS 8

They're big.

That's what we know about blue whales, the largest animals that ever lived. They're big. They average eighty to ninety feet long, from the tip of the snout to the center of their tails. The largest one officially recorded came in at 98 feet long. That's about as long as three school buses. They typically weigh between 50 and 150 tons. You'd have to gather at least five hundred people to have a mass that large.

Everything about them is big. Their hearts are the size of small cars. Their lungs hold about 1200 gallons of air. Their stomachs can hold a ton of food. Their mouths house a three-ton tongue and can envelope more than 15,000 gallons of water and food. Their skulls can be nineteen feet long, and their brains weigh fifteen pounds. They sing songs louder than a jackhammer, heard for hundreds of miles. At birth, their babies already weigh around 5,000 pounds and measure more than twenty feet long. Adults eat four tons of food a day, and nursing babies can put on about ten pounds of body weight every hour. At weaning, the baby is about half the size of an adult, having grown at least ten times their birth weight.

They are enormous.

Despite all their power and wonder as God's largest animal creatures, we nearly hunted them to extinction in the twentieth century. In just sixty years, more than a third of a million blue whales were captured and killed, reducing their numbers to just a few thousand. Since whaling stopped, blue whales have rebounded, but they remain a tiny fraction of their former numbers.

God placed Adam in the Garden of Eden to work it and keep it. The word translated keep *is the Hebrew term* shamar, *which carries a meaning of protecting and treasuring and saving. It's a word used for protecting a city, treasuring of God's covenant, and warning against evil. When God appeared to Jacob as he fled from his brother, He told him, "Behold, I am with you and will keep [*shamar*] you wherever you go, and will bring you back to this land" (Genesis 28:15). Humanity is placed here on this earth to guard it and to treasure it and to save it.*

Thank God humanity came to its senses before wiping out these mightiest of God's creatures. Blue whales, like all other works of the Lord, proclaim the glory of God. They reflect His power and majesty. For all the sprawling mass of a blue whale, God Almighty is yet bigger and holds them in his hand. We do well when we treasure and guard and save the gifts he gives.

Here is the sea, great and wide,
which teems with creatures innumerable,
living things both small and great.
There go the ships,
and Leviathan, which you formed to play in it.
These all look to you,
to give them their food in due season.
May the glory of the Lord endure forever;
may the Lord rejoice in his works.
(Psalm 104:25-27, 31)

9
VIRTUES OF THE
UNCERTAIN

The quest is a difficult calling for people. The quest asks us to embrace the unknown. No matter who we are, we don't have all the answers. We don't know what the final truth about creation will look like. Other than our ultimate goal of seeking God, we're not even sure if we're on the right track. Rather than committing to the dogma of answers or positions or arguments, we must instead commit to continue seeking the truth. We commit to a way that we believe will lead us to truth and life.

In the modern creation/evolution debate, however, we are conditioned to expect something quite different. People want good arguments, compelling evidence, and settled questions. People want the truth that shows them the way to life, but every faction (young-age creationism, old-age creationism, theistic evolution, etc.) has their own truth that contradicts everyone else's. We all claim that we already have all the important answers and that everybody else's position doesn't have any answers. If one of those factions has your full allegiance, you might not think much of the quest. You already have all the answers. You don't need to seek them.

On the other hand, there is a quiet majority of Christians out there that's a bit different. In 2012, BioLogos, the leading Christian advocate of theistic evolution, commissioned a poll from the Barna group to identify attitudes towards creation and evolution among American Protestant pastors. Barna conducted 743 phone interviews, and the results confirmed that the majority of pastors (54%) are young-age creationists.[62] Only 18% of pastors surveyed identified as theistic evolutionists. If you've kept up with these sorts of surveys, that should come as no surprise at all.

What is surprising and unique about this survey is the uncertainty of American pastors. Each category that pastors identified with was further divided into "core" (pastors who were really certain) and "leaning" (pastors who were not certain). Among the young-age creationist pastors, only 35% claimed to be certain of their position on origins. Old-age creationist pastors were more likely to be sure of their position (47% were certain), and theistic evolutionist pastors were the most uncertain of them all (17% were certain). Add to that the 12% of pastors who declined to identify as young-age, old-age, or theistic evolutionist, and you find that a whopping 70% of American Protestant pastors are not sure about their position on origins. They still have questions.

That huge fraction is a lot like me. Most of them made a commitment to a position despite mysteries, problems, and unanswered questions. Even though some Christians might find the uncertainty of the quest distasteful and off-putting, I would guess a majority would resonate pretty deeply with what I've tried to describe here, even if they don't share my young-age creationist commitment.

No matter who we are, we don't know everything. We all want to understand the world and our Lord better. So we commit first to a way of seeking the truth. Part of that way, as I've described here, is asking questions both of scripture and science, but there's more.

The Christian life is not simply an academic exercise. Our calling to follow Christ means that we are being shaped into his image. The quest cannot simply be a quest for answers. It must be a quest to become like Jesus. That means that we must practice the basic Christian virtues in order to conform ourselves to the image of Jesus.

Believe

The simplest virtue we must practice—the one we need before we can even begin our quest—is faith. Faith is not merely an attitude of optimism, nor is it a settled and learned conclusion based on evidence. Those things may be a part of faith, but faith is much more than that. Faith is a confidence in God and in his son Jesus Christ.

Faith is knowing more than just facts or arguments or reasons. Faith is knowing a person. Because of that, faith isn't something that I can give you. I can describe Christian theology and its intellectual appeal. I can explain how Christianity helps me make sense of the world. I can even tell you about my personal encounters with God. All of that might be very interesting to you. It might even make you curious to know more, but until you experience it for yourself, all the explanations and arguments in the world don't make sense of it.

Faith is not just knowing a person though. Faith is active. Faith acts on its knowledge and confidence. Faith is obedience. Faith without that obedience isn't true faith. We can't confine our belief in Christ to intellectual conversations or debates about theism. Our faith must be put to work. The quest is one way we put our faith to work. The quest cannot begin without it.

This is a really important point that we need to consider very carefully. We cannot understand God and his creation without first believing and acting on that belief. The author of Hebrews says it this way:

> And without faith it is impossible to please him, for whoever would draw near to God must believe that he exists and that he rewards those who seek him. (Hebrews 11:6)

Ponder that for a moment, because it's profound but rarely understood. You cannot draw near to God—you cannot succeed on the quest—if you don't already believe that God is there waiting to reward you. The quest is not a quest *for* faith. Faith must precede the quest. Faith comes first.

The quest, with all its discoveries and signposts that confirm that we're on the right track, does not make you believe. It might grow your faith, as you become more familiar with the Lord and more comfortable with his providence. But the Bible makes it clear that faith comes first. If you want answers from God, you have to believe.

I don't want to discount the power of evidence or science as something the Holy Spirit could use to inspire that first spark of faith, but that's not the primary purpose of the quest. The quest is seeking God. It begins with the faith that he exists. He's real, and he speaks to us. The purpose of the quest is not to convince other people that creationism is true. That might be a happy side effect, and we might even see lots of people being convinced to join us. But it's not the purpose. Whoever wants to find God on the quest must first believe that God is there to be found.

Confess

The second step on the quest is humility. I've already mentioned that lots of people and organizations in the creation/evolution debate present themselves as having all the answers, or at least all the important answers. In my experience, a lot of those answers don't really hold up. Some do, of course, but not all. As I described in the previous chapter, there are many big questions that haven't really been answered yet. To seek answers, you have to confess that you don't have them, and that takes humility.

It also takes guts. When I first got into creationism, there was sort of a trend of creationists publishing papers that corrected old creationist arguments.[63] I quite enjoyed it, and I even contributed one of my own. My subject was one that was near and dear to my heart at the time: living plesiosaurs!

When I was in high school, I happened to come across a copy of a creationist book on dinosaurs with a vivid color photograph of what appeared to be the recently-dead carcass of a plesiosaur. According to the book, the carcass was discovered near New Zealand by a Japanese fishing boat called the *Zuiyo-maru*. They had taken photographs, tissue samples, and then dumped the carcass overboard. I was so excited, I wrote a report about the carcass and living plesiosaurs for my tenth grade English class.

Years later, I made contact with a person who had a copy of the scientific report on the carcass that was published in Japan.[64] As I read the English articles in the report, I was disappointed to discover the overwhelming evidence that the carcass was actually a really rotten shark. So I did what I felt I ought to do. Even though my high school paper was just between me and the teacher, I still felt responsible for promoting false information. So I wrote a letter to the editor of the *Creation Research Society Quarterly*, summarizing the evidence that the *Zuiyo-maru* carcass was just a shark.[65]

I was surprised to discover later that the *Quarterly* wanted to publish rebuttals to my summary. The rebuttals continued for several years. Some of them said my paper was illogical (it was not) and that you can't trust the testimony of an evolutionist (since the people describing the carcass were evolutionists). The most discouraging part of all of it was receiving a message from another creationist who complained that we young people were taking away all the "good arguments."

In a climate of culture war, admitting that we don't have answers is pretty risky. It's akin to telling the enemy that we don't actually have any weapons or defenses. On the other hand, it's also really disarming. I've shocked a number of theistic evolutionists by simply admitting that I don't have all the answers to the mysteries of creation science. Why anyone should be shocked by that I don't know. It's not like evolutionists know everything about evolution! I think this surprised reaction says that there's something very defective about this debate. Why should we ever pretend to have all the answers? What kind of arrogance is that? And what kind of arrogance complains about the loss of a "good argument" that is actually a *false* argument?

This isn't just a creationist issue either. The history of science is littered with wrong ideas. When you think about it, the vast majority of ideas proposed over the history of science have been wrong. Science makes progress, though, because scientists root out those errors and push forward to better explanations. Chances are, your favorite hypothesis in science will be proved wrong one day. We all need to be prepared for that by practicing humility.

If you want to succeed on the quest, just admit the truth: We don't know everything. Commit yourself to seeking answers to the hardest questions. Be willing to admit when you got something wrong. Don't hold onto arguments out of obsession or stubbornness or pride.

Persist

One more virtue you'll need on your quest is patience. Our modern culture, with the internet at our fingertips, is addicted to having everything right now, including all the answers we want. Early in my career, I mapped out the kind of research that I thought creationists needed to work on to make good progress on the quest in the area of biology. I figured if we applied ourselves, in 5-10 years, we would have some big breakthroughs that would answer some of these big questions. That was dumb. I was arrogant. We've made a lot of progress for sure,[66] but most of the hard questions remain unanswered.

The culture is always pushing though. I've lost track of the number of people who try to debate me by asking me a bunch of questions, and when I say that I don't know, they seem smugly satisfied, as if they just won the debate. Or they get angry. Over and over, I've heard people tell me, "You have to explain this." They always seem puzzled when I don't care about their smugness or their demands, and I don't change my opinion. This insistence that creationists have to solve everything right now is just more arrogance, and you don't have to fall for it.

The reality is that making progress in any discipline takes time. Revolutions are rare. Much more common is the slow and steady pace of incremental discoveries that add just a little bit more to our understanding. My favorite example of this is Belshazzar.

The book of Daniel describes Belshazzar as the final king of Babylon before the Medes and the Persians conquered the city. Ancient historical records tell us that the final king of Babylon was actually a guy named Nabonidus. When Babylonian records were discovered in the 1800s and deciphered in the early 1900s, we found out that Nabonidus had a son that he left in charge of Babylon while Nabonidus was away. That son's name was Belshazzar. Daniel was right after all. Belshazzar was indeed in charge of Babylon, even though Nabonidus was the king of the empire. This is why Belshazzar offered to make Daniel "third" in the kingdom if he could interpret the writing on the wall. Belshazzar himself was second, and his father was first.

Now that's not the only historical discrepancy with the book of Daniel, but the story of Nabonidus and Belshazzar still encourages me not to jump to conclusions. It reminds me that we know so little when we think we know so much. Most importantly, these discoveries didn't just happen overnight. We knew about Nabonidus for centuries before we discovered the name of his son Belshazzar. When people demand that I explain some data that is difficult for creationists, I just smile and remember Belshazzar.

Patience also works to nurture your faith. The cultural pressure to answer everything right now makes people frantic. Young people especially fall victim to that crazy impulse that we have to figure it all out. It's easy to get frustrated when you can't figure things out right away. Unfortunately, some of that frustration can turn to panic. When people panic, they make poor decisions, but in this arena, they think they're making good decisions. Too many people walk away from the faith because they have a lingering question about some science they can't explain. Fossil forests, genomics, dinosaur feathers, I've heard it all. Don't be that person.

Stop for a moment and think about your own faith first. Pray for relief. Remember the example of Job: He demanded a court hearing with God to plead his case, but when God arrived, that demand was quickly forgotten. Don't expect God to answer the questions nagging at you. Instead, expect God to deliver you from doubt however He will.

I would also encourage those caught in this anxiety for answers to think about the progress of creationism. It's easy to get caught in the spiral of doubt when you fixate on what we don't know, but pondering the path we've already covered can be immensely encouraging. Creationism's progress has been amazing. Research conducted in my lifetime at Mt. St. Helens, Grand Canyon, and Specimen Ridge has been fantastic.[67] The ongoing dinosaur excavation at the Hanson Research Station in Wyoming is amazing![68] Creationists could barely dream of these things 100 years ago. Hasn't God been faithful thus far? What surprises will tomorrow bring? Don't you want to stick around and find out?

Faith, humility, and patience are important virtues for the quest, and they can help us deal with cantankerous critics. But there is still more than that to the quest.

There is an even more excellent way.

ADOREMUS 9

We all learned about butterfly metamorphosis in elementary school. We learned about the caterpillars, little wormy creatures with little wormy legs. We learned that these voracious leaf eaters grow to full size then transform into a chrysalis, from which emerges a butterfly, so different from its earlier life, one might even suspect they were two different creatures altogether. This is a radical change in form, this metamorphosis.

While still a ravenous caterpillar, its body houses a big gut for digesting all that food and a group of cells called imaginal discs that do nothing for the caterpillar. The transformation begins when the caterpillar reaches its full size and its "juvenile hormone" begins to disappear. The caterpillar finds a safe spot and secretes a little silk nub. Holding onto that silk button, the caterpillar sheds its skin one last time revealing the shiny surface of a chrysalis.

Inside that chrysalis, the animal rapidly alters much of its body and structure. Some organs merely grow larger while the gut shrinks and moves to a new location. The imaginal discs undergo the most radical change of all, rapidly growing and developing into the features of the adult butterfly, the legs and wings and body.

The chrysalis lasts for at least five days, and some as long as three weeks. Desert caterpillars can remain a chrysalis until the rains return, occasionally waiting years. In monarch butterflies, the chrysalis turns transparent, revealing the curled up butterfly within. As the butterfly emerges, it tears open the chrysalis with its legs, crawls out, and hangs upside down. Its wings at this point are still tiny, but in the next few minutes it will pump fluid from its fattened abdomen into its wings, stretching the wings and shrinking the abdomen.

At the end of days, in the Revelation, John witnessed the passing of this world, in a moment, as the God of all creation appeared on his great white throne. Earth and sky fled from his presence, the sea was no more, and a new heaven and new earth appeared, with a New Jerusalem descending from heaven. Death will be defeated, and there will be no more crying or sorrow or mourning.

Seated on his throne in this new city, God declares, "Behold, I make all things new." All of creation will undergo a metamorphosis from a fallen, sinful world into a glorious city where God will dwell with his people. We see now dimly in the metamorphosis of the butterfly a shadow of things to come when we will be like him, for we shall see him as he is.

> Therefore, if anyone is in Christ, he is a new creation. The old has passed away; behold, the new has come. All this is from God, who through Christ reconciled us to himself and gave us the ministry of reconciliation. (II Corinthians 5:17-18)

10
THE MORE
EXCELLENT WAY

The apostle Paul first visited the ancient Greek city of Corinth on his second missionary journey. He spent eighteen months with the Corinthian believers teaching and training them in the gospel, but when he left, the church fell into disagreement and strife. They argued over which gospel preacher was better, whether to eat meat offered to idols, and how and when to speak in tongues. They even tried to sue each other in court to settle their differences. Paul rebuked them in his first epistle by reminding them of what's really important.

> If I speak in the tongues of men and of angels, but have not love, I am a noisy gong or a clanging cymbal. And if I have prophetic powers, and understand all mysteries and all knowledge, and if I have all faith, so as to remove mountains, but have not love, I am nothing. (I Cor. 13:1-2)

This is one of those passages that sounds so familiar that we almost lose sight of the profound meaning in Paul's words. For Paul, even if you succeeded in resolving the debate over speaking in tongues and you had the right answer, you would still get it all wrong without love. Even more disturbing for us scientists, knowing all there is to know about something is worthless without love. Having all faith and prophetic power to understand the Word of God gets you nothing without love.

Love is everything.

I freely confess that that's a hard thing for me to read. I have been anything and everything except loving. I have pursued understanding with the devotion of a zealot. I have scorned error. I have broken fellowship. With some folks, I haven't even tried to have fellowship. They're just too different from me. They weren't worth the bother.

Because of that, Paul says that I am nothing. My career, my work, twenty years of effort are all pointless. As long as I use my talents and abilities recklessly to divide and alienate believers, I continue to be nothing. Jesus Christ told us the world would know we are Christians by our love for one another. Looking at my life, no one would have guessed.

Now I need to re-orient my quest. The quest is not just a journey to understanding. The quest is part of our Christian walk. It can't be divorced from the most basic virtues, the kind of virtues we should have learned in vacation Bible school or children's church. Because if we can't practice becoming *like* Christ on our quest *to* Christ, then the quest is pointless.

Where do we begin? How does a middle-aged creationist stop a lifetime of bad habits and learn to love? It's probably good to go back to the basic commands of the Bible. Love God and love your neighbor. How can we incorporate that kind of love into our quest? I'm not even going to pretend to be an expert here, but I have a few thoughts.

Love God

When I first began dating the woman who would become my wife, I remember sitting on my porch after dinner and talking to her on our second date. Now I'm not much of a social talker, that's for sure, but that night, we kept talking long after the sun went down. The mosquitos feasted on us, and we kept talking. I think it was three in the morning before we finally gave up trying to stay awake, and she went home. We were getting to know each other, and there was so much to discover. I didn't really want to stop.

Just like that night on my porch, the quest to understand God and his creation is an act of love all by itself. To orient and focus your attention on another person, especially on God, is love. To study God's works in order to discover more about him is love. This world is not just a rock we inhabit. God's creation is an expression of himself. It is magnificent, always thrilling and surprising those who pay attention. God's beauty, wonder, and power are out there waiting for us to find. From the tiniest bits of DNA to the grand scale of the universe itself, we only have to open our eyes to see His wonders.

All too often, though, we take creation for granted. Even worse, when we see it used to promote evolution, we might even get angry. Back in 2015, when the skeletal remains of a human form called *Homo naledi* were first announced to the world, I remember one creationist responded, "Here we go again." The *Homo naledi* discovery in a cave north of Johannesburg, South Africa is the richest hominin fossil discovery on the entire continent.[69] When the ongoing excavations are complete, there will be thousands of bones from dozens of bodies. You know who knew about those bones before they were discovered? God knew. He made those bones. He made those people. They're part of his creation. How could a Christian ever see such an amazing discovery and not fall down in gratitude and worship to our Creator for giving us the ability to find these glimpses of his glory? How could we ever say, "Here we go again"?

The *Homo naledi* bones have been down there in the Rising Star Cave for thousands of years, right under the noses of four million residents of Johannesburg. What wonders of God are right outside your door? What amazing discoveries are lurking in your own back yard? God is waiting for you to find them.

Give thanks to the Lord for eyes to see and ears to hear his glory. Join with all creation as we lift our voices in praise to our God and creator. The stars and planets declare the glory of God. The sky shows his handiwork. The stones cry out. We're caught in the middle of a symphony bigger than you or I could ever imagine, and in the midst of it all, God made us with minds to comprehend and hearts that can reach out to him. Be grateful every day. Be grateful *for* every day. Love God with all your heart, with all your soul, and with all your mind.

Love Your Neighbor

Jesus told us if we love him, we'll keep his commandments, and the second greatest commandment is to love your neighbor. How do we love other people with creationist research?

I think one obvious answer is that sharing the truth about creation with people is an act of love. It's like sharing the gospel. We see the wonders of God's creation, and we want to tell people. We can't keep silent. God's work is worth sharing, whether it's his personal work in our lives or creating and sustaining the universe. We should celebrate and invite others to do the same.

We as a church also need to think more deliberately about how science can be used directly to love our neighbors. Crisis pregnancy centers are examples of this approach. Instead of just telling women not to have abortions, pregnancy centers provide support and ministry to women who choose to keep their babies. Jesus definitely spoke out against the abuses of the religious leaders of his day, but he also provided practical, compassionate ministry of healing, feeding, and occasionally raising the dead. He was not merely an advocate.

In the world of science, it's very easy for us to get lost in political debate without thinking about how the church should be present in science. There are many issues that Christians care about that are connected directly to science, including medical research with embryonic stem cells, environmental stewardship and care, and public health and vaccinations. We need more Christians involved with these critical issues, providing moral options and leading the way in research. That's not every Christian's job, but the body of Christ as a whole needs to be present in science.

Because of that need to minister to others, we must not discourage our young scientists. Too often, I think creationists cast a very suspicious eye on science, fearing that children will be brainwashed. We've all heard the sad stories of smart kids that go to college and then tumble down that slippery slope to unbelief. While that's good reason to be careful of scholarly work, we should walk *with* the next generation and disciple them. Help them remain faithful to Christ while they pursue their scientific studies. Nurture in them the faith they need so that they can hold fast to the truth even when they feel like doubting. Let them ask hard questions, even if you don't have the answers. Remind them of what we do know. Remind them of the living savior that we serve. Remind them of the great cloud of witnesses cheering us on in the faith. Remind them that they are not alone.

Most importantly of all, don't be an obstacle to the gospel. As Paul tried to explain to the Corinthians the spiritual significance of the idol meat dispute, he made what I consider to be kind of a shocking statement.

> Food will not commend us to God. We are no worse off if we do not eat, and no better off if we do. But take care that this right of yours does not somehow become a stumbling block to the weak. For if anyone sees you who have knowledge eating in an idol's temple, will he not be encouraged, if his conscience is weak, to eat food offered to idols? And so by your knowledge this weak person is destroyed, the brother for whom Christ died. Thus, sinning against your brothers and wounding their conscience when it is weak, you sin against Christ. Therefore, if food makes my brother stumble, I will never eat meat, lest I make my brother stumble. (I Corinthians 8:8-13)

Paul's notion of freedom is completely antithetical to the radical individualism of modern western culture. Today, you're encouraged to be "true to yourself" and do whatever's "right for you" regardless of what anyone else thinks. For Paul, freedom in Christ was bounded by his responsibility to those of weaker conscience. Paul is willing to give up his freedom for the sake of others. He will not allow his freedom to become a stumbling block to someone else.

How can we apply this to creationism? We must remember that even though the creation/evolution issue is important, it is not the gospel. Our salvation depends on what we do with Jesus Christ, not what we do with the age of the earth. We cannot make our stand on creationism or theistic evolution or any scientific matter a condition of salvation.

I understand that when pushed, there isn't a single person in this debate who will actually claim that having the correct view on creation is required for salvation, and I don't want to imply that anyone is deliberately distorting the gospel of Jesus. Nevertheless, our zeal for creation often speaks louder than our words. Every side of this debate blames the others for leading people away from the gospel. Theistic evolutionists complain that the supposedly sloppy science of creationists prevents them from sharing the gospel with their scientific colleagues. Creationists complain that theistic evolutionists have compromised the gospel with the anti-theistic philosophy of evolution that is totally incompatible with the truth of God's Word. So we don't explicitly add creation to the gospel, but we sure do imply it by the sharp condemnation we level at the other sides.

On the other hand, creation as a doctrine is really important to our Christian identity, and I don't want to pretend otherwise. The creation of Adam and Eve in the image of God and their subsequent fall into sin have been part of Christian theology since the time of the New Testament. Still, if it came down to a choice between accepting young-age creationism or going to hell, I certainly hope we could all condemn that choice. If my zeal for young-age creationism creates that kind of theological dilemma, then I need to re-examine my priorities. Creationism is not the gospel. I would rather someone believe on the Lord Jesus Christ as a theistic evolutionist than deliberately choose an eternity separated from God. That shouldn't even be something we have to think about. At least I can pray for theistic evolutionists who are true Christians and claim Jesus' promise that the Holy Spirit will lead us into truth. I must not allow my zeal for creation to overshadow my zeal for salvation. The good news that Jesus Christ died for my sins is far more important than how old the earth is.

To love my neighbor, I need to keep my theological priorities straight. I need to make crystal clear precisely what the gospel is.

Love Your Enemies

Jesus had one other command about loving that is not something people like to think about. When he proclaimed that loving our neighbor was the second greatest commandment, some scribe immediately asked him who our neighbor was. When he told us to love our enemies, no one asked who that was. They all knew, and we still do.

Enemies are those who work against you. They work to prevent you from doing what you want to do. Worse, they might even work to prevent you from doing what ought to be done. Enemies come in all shapes and sizes, but we rarely like to admit that they exist. We like to keep up the façade of loving and getting along with everyone, but we sure grumble about them anyway.

In this debate, with the battle lines clear, our enemies are easy to recognize. But there are other, more subtle enemies. People on our own "team" who have very different priorities than we do, or people who simply don't like us. Sometimes simple misunderstandings can lead to suspicion and resentment. In young-age creationism, we have a lot of people who are used to going against the mainstream, and most of us don't have any problem voicing unpopular opinions, no matter how much it might annoy other creationists. There are big, obvious enemies, and there are "those people." And we have to love them all.

How do we ignore our egos and learn to love? A first step, I think, is to listen. Too often we read an article or book, make some quick judgments based on our expectations or interpretations of the book, and then start listing all the ways our enemies got it wrong. We tell ourselves that it's loving to give them the truth they clearly don't understand, even if we have to deliver it with a sledgehammer.

It's rare to find people who really, really disagree about something important sitting down and talking. When it does happen, when our enemies are speaking, we mostly spend our time mentally composing our rebuttals. We almost never practice the art of listening, really listening, really trying to understand where our enemies are coming from.

Wouldn't that be an interesting experiment though? Imagine someone coming to you trying to pick a fight, probably with the entire conversation already rehearsed in their head. Then imagine you just listen and nod and agree where you can and thank them for helping you understand their position better. Remember where Proverbs tells us that a soft answer turns away wrath? I think that's what that looks like.

Maybe the first step in this process is not talking about your disagreements but just talking. Discover your enemy not as a position but as a person. Look for those deeper values and issues that motivate your enemies. Try to figure out what makes them tick, and then try to think through your own life and values as you formulate a response. Above all, remember the power of the gospel. Grace can cover all our sins, even the sins of our enemies. The words of your response can bring life or death. You can minister grace or condemnation. I think the more we really try to understand each other, the more people will see Jesus.

Once you know your enemy, not from the pages of a book or article but as a living, breathing child of God, you can portray them fairly. Far too often in debate, we'll put up strawmen to beat on, all the while pretending that they are accurate portrayals of our enemies. We refuse to acknowledge the weaknesses of our own position, while magnifying the perceived defects of our enemies. This is not honest, and it does not honor Jesus Christ, who is the truth. We must learn to portray ourselves and our enemies truthfully, even if that leaves us vulnerable to "attack." Jesus is big enough to take care of us.

In all of this, we must again remember our weaker brother. People don't hold positions because they're stupid or evil. People have reasons for what they believe. Sometimes people have even carefully deliberated on their beliefs, no matter how wrong those beliefs might be. When we speak to our enemies or about our enemies, we must always consider the overwhelming importance of the gospel. If pushing an issue is pushing someone away from Christ, then we need to stop. Winning an argument and being right is not worth someone's soul.

Finally, my brothers and sisters, let us hear the conclusion of the whole matter: Love God, love your neighbor, and love your enemy. If we say we love God and hate our brothers and sisters, we deceive ourselves and the truth is not in us. Love is not an option. It's the most important command that we must obey, even if we have to re-learn everything we think we know. It's worth it. Jesus is worth it, and the quest is pointless without it.

EPILOGUE

When the apostle Paul wrote to the Roman church, he had never visited them before. Hints from the text suggest that Paul was still residing in Corinth during his second missionary journey when the letter was written. Unlike the rest of his letters, Romans is an introduction to people Paul does not know and most likely an introduction to his most basic gospel message.

As he wrapped up the good news of Jesus, Paul encouraged the Roman Christians with this passage,

> I appeal to you therefore, brothers, by the mercies of God, to present your bodies as a living sacrifice, holy and acceptable to God, which is your spiritual worship. Do not be conformed to this world, but be transformed by the renewal of your mind, that by testing you may discern what is the will of God, what is good and acceptable and perfect. (Romans 12:1-2)

As I look at these words two thousand years later, they speak as clearly and vividly to me as they did to the Romans. They remind me that everything I have belongs to Christ. This isn't *my* quest. This is the quest that Jesus laid out for me.

Since it is ultimately his quest, there is no part that I can (pretend to) withhold from the lordship of Christ or the scrutiny of the Holy Spirit. I cannot say that science is just fine as it is and does not need the renewing of the Holy Spirit. Nor can I say that my biblical interpretation is perfect. If the Spirit wants to speak anew through the Bible, I should be prepared to listen and transform myself accordingly. If the Spirit wants to challenge my scientific conclusions, no matter how certain they seem, I need to listen.

But this is more than just a passive willingness to change if Jesus wants us to. Paul encourages us to actively avoid conforming to the world and to actively be transformed by the renewing of our minds. We should seek this transformation. We should seek better understandings of scripture *and* of science. Nothing can be excluded.

Even after writing this book and living this quest, I don't think I can yet comprehend the magnitude of the calling of Christ. His ways are not my ways. His understanding is perfect, and mine is not. Into those massive, yawning gaps of my own ignorance, he pours faith and hope. Faith in what I know of Him already, and hope for what I will learn tomorrow.

Every discovery in this quest, every new tidbit of knowledge, gives me a surge of excitement and hope. That hope reminds me that I'm on the right path, at least for today. I'm not always optimistic, of course. Some days I wonder if we'll ever figure anything out. Then something new comes along, and I put my eyes back on my goal and not on the storms around me. And sometimes, thanks to a kind word from a colleague or a student, I am reminded of how far we've already come. May God continue to bless this quest.

Remember though that these three remain, faith, hope, and love, but the greatest of these is love. That is what the Holy Spirit wants to transform the most, not our knowledge or understanding but the way we treat each other. Before you try to win that argument, ask yourself if your love is really worth the cost of winning.

I want to leave you with a few final thoughts. I know for certain that some readers disagree with my quest. Some might even be angry right now with me. Maybe they think I'm a hypocrite for preaching love. Maybe they think I'm stupid (or something even more sinister) for rejecting all their "good arguments" against evolution. Or maybe they think I'm hateful or ignorant for rejecting theistic evolution. Some are probably thinking right now about the rebuttal they want to publish on their websites or even in formal book reviews. How can I love even these?

First of all, though I remain committed to my position as a young-age creationist, I have to admit that I could be wrong. As I look back over the history of science and scholarship, I discover that people have always been wrong about a lot of things, often in ways they could barely comprehend. Whether we're talking about the structure of the cosmos or spontaneous generation, even the most respected Christian thinkers were dead wrong about a lot of things.

I'm no different than they were. I'm probably wrong about a lot of things and wrong in ways I can't even imagine. As I look back at the world of the early nineteenth century, I wonder what humanity will "know" two hundred years from now. And how stupid will I seem then?

As I think about my own errors, I wonder if the value of the quest is not in the discoveries we make (which may turn out to be wrong, too) but in the discipline we practice in bringing everything in our lives under the authority of Jesus Christ. I also wonder if that might also be true of others on quests of old-earth creationism or even (dare I say it?) theistic evolution? If we together confess our ignorance and commit to seeking Christ, who is the truth, surely he will bless. After all, he did promise that those who seek will find.

Second, I make no apology for the firmness of my beliefs, and I hope you won't make apology for yours, as much as they may annoy me. What I've written here is a lifetime of conviction. This isn't something I've flippantly adopted for the sake of convenience (it's anything but) or respect of peers (there isn't any). If we ever hope to make progress on any of our quests, we cannot adopt the way of the world where political opponents demonize their enemies and shout them to silence. The bullying and shaming of social media mob rule is not the way of Christ.

More than just having firm beliefs though, I hope you might also think carefully about why you hold your firm beliefs. Having conviction or commitment is very different from being stubborn. Be willing to think more carefully about what you believe. Be ready to reconsider even your most precious ideas. That is the part of the quest I hope we can all agree with. We're all ignorant, and we all need to seek the truth of Christ. It's also the part that is the hardest for our pride to swallow: I could be wrong.

Lastly, to all the students reading this book, be encouraged! God is faithful! His creation is magnificent! Answers may seem far off, but you can't even imagine what discoveries and wonders tomorrow will bring. Speak to the earth, and it will tell you. Ask the animals, and they will teach you. Listen to the stars, and hear them praise the creator. Be strong in your faith. Be curious with your mind. Be diligent with your work. Seek and you *will* find.

Let us all follow Paul's ancient encouragement to Christians he has not met (us). Let us renew our commitment in faith to transform our minds in submission to the ministry of the Holy Spirit and the lordship of Jesus Christ.

May the God of peace be with you all.

Amen.

APPENDIX
JOINING THE QUEST

Let's say you're a student, and you're excited about what you've read here, and you want to get involved. What now? I was hoping I might reach a few of you, so let's talk about what you can do.

First of all, stay in school. I know that's trite, but it's true. You need to get educated and trained. Like I said, don't expect to be able to learn a discipline just from reading books. Get involved. You have to get your hands dirty.

What should you study? The sky's the limit. What are you interested in? Creationism is still very wide open, and just about any field of study can make substantial contributions. The only specific advice I would give is not to hide from conventional science. Don't choose engineering or horticulture or biotechnology because you think evolutionary biology or geology will be too difficult for a creationist. At least try to get relevant training. That's not to denigrate any of those fields, if that's your passion. Just don't feel like you have to settle.

If you're looking at undergraduate institutions, and you want creationist-based training friendly to the quest, there are several options. I hesitate to even mention them, because I'll leave someone out, but here goes. Check out Cedarville University or the Master's University for geology. Southwestern Adventist University could get you plugged into the dinosaur excavations at the Hanson Station.

The Center for Creation Studies at Liberty University would be glad to have you study biology there. You're also welcome to come on down to Chattanooga to study at Bryan College, Southern Adventist University, or Covenant College and work with me here at Core Academy of Science as a research intern. There are many other possibilities, but these are just a few that come to mind.

Next, you're going to need some creationist training. Here are some books you'll find helpful, but the content is biased to biology. You should probably ask someone else about any other discipline.

Paley, William. 2008. *Natural Theology*. Oxford: Oxford University Press. Originally published in 1802, this book is a classic of old school natural theology (hence the title), which argues for the existence and attributes of God based on contrivances of living things. Read the book carefully and pay attention especially to Paley's treatment of natural evil.

Darwin, Charles. 2009. *The Annotated Origin*. Annotated by James T. Costa. Cambridge, MA: The Belknap Press. Yes, you should read *Origin of Species*. Don't be shy. Costa's version reprints the first edition (the best) and includes lots of commentary to help you understand what you're reading.

Roberts, Jon H. 1988. *Darwinism and the Divine in America*. Notre Dame, IN: University of Notre Dame Press. This is a good book to help you understand how the people who would eventually be called "creationists" responded to Darwin's *Origin*.

Price, George McCready. 1923. *The New Geology*. Mountain View, CA: Pacific Press Publishing Association. This is a seminal work in creationist geology. Much of Price's work has been modified or rejected by creationists over the years, but many of these ideas linger on in creationist folklore (stuff you've heard, but you can't remember where). It's important to know what these ideas are, and where they came from.

Clark, Harold W. 1946. *The New Diluvialism.* Angwin, CA: Science Publications. This is the beginning of non-Price creationist geology. It also introduces the concept of ecological zonation as an explanation for the fossil record.

Marsh, Frank L. 1947. *Evolution, Creation and Science,* revised edition. Washington, DC: Review and Herald Publishing. This is a classical statement of creationist biology written by the third major Seventh-day Adventist creationist of 1900-1950 (the other two are Price and Clark). Marsh is a pioneer in the study of the "created kind."

Numbers, Ronald L. 2006. *The Creationists,* expanded edition. Cambridge, MA: Harvard University Press. This incredibly helpful history of twentieth century creationism paints modern young-age creationism as an outgrowth of Seventh-day Adventism but still gives a decent record of the who, what, and when. The Center for Adventist Research at Andrews University has Numbers's original correspondence after he passed the manuscript around to be read by a number of the individuals featured in the book. Without exception, they said they didn't remember things being so dramatic, so keep that in mind as you read.

Whitcomb, John C. and Henry M. Morris. 1961. *The Genesis Flood.* Phillipsburg, NJ: Presbyterian and Reformed Publishers. This book helped to launch the twentieth century creationist revival in the 1960s, although much of the scientific content is recycled from Price and Marsh. It's still worth reading.

Dembski, William A. 1998. *The Design Inference.* Cambridge: Cambridge University Press. One of the books that launched the "Intelligent Design" movement. It's really intriguing stuff.

Wise, Kurt P. 2002. *Faith, Form, and Time.* Nashville, TN: Broadman & Holman Publishers. It's old, but it has a good overview of the entire creation model.

Wood, Todd Charles and Megan J. Murray. 2003. *Understanding the Pattern of Life.* Nashville, TN: Broadman & Holman Publishers. Yes, this is mine, but it's a helpful but very, very dated overview of created kinds and biology. Think of it as an update of Marsh's book.

Garner, Paul. 2009. *The New Creationism.* Darlington, England: Evangelical Press. Also out of date, but another useful update on the creation model.

Snelling, Andrew A. 2009. *Earth's Catastrophic Past.* Dallas, TX: Institute for Creation Research. Again, this one is out of date, but it's still a good update of Price, Clark, and Whitcomb and Morris.

Brand, Leonard and Arthur Chadwick. 2016. *Faith, Reason, and Earth History*, third edition. Berrien Springs, MI: Andrews University Press. A much more recent work focusing mostly on biology and geology from two seasoned creationist researchers. Highly recommended.

Finally, you need to be part of a community. That means minimally going to church, and not one of those big megachurches where you can hide in the pew and remain completely anonymous. Surround yourself with believers, especially believers who are not scholars. I can't tell you what a blessing it was to be a member of Wayne Hills

Baptist Church while I was a student. Those people cared about me, and that church spiritually protected me from the difficulties of my studies, my own discouragements, and the basic challenges of life. Don't try to go it alone. Surround yourself with godly friends and mentors.

You'll also want to stay plugged into the world of creationism. I recommend you subscribe to the two big creationist journals, *Creation Research Society Quarterly* from the Creation Research Society (http://creationresearch.org) and *Journal of Creation* from Creation Ministries International (http://creation.com). The papers in these journals aren't always worth reading, but it's important to be aware of what other creationists are saying. Answers in Genesis also publishes a free, online journal called *Answers Research Journal*, which you can access at their website (http://answersingenesis.org).

You also need to attend creationist conferences. I recommend two: The annual Origins conference and the International Conference on Creationism (ICC). Origins is sponsored by the Creation Biology Society (http://creationbiology.org) and the Creation Geology Society and features research presentations from a small but dedicated group of creation researchers. The ICC (http://creationicc.org) is held every five years and draws from a much wider range of creationist scholars.

Last but certainly not least, if you're itching to dig even deeper than anything on this list, if you really want to push the limit, you should check out a Creation Retreat from Core Academy of Science (http://coresci.org). We hold these retreats annually in locations around the country, and each one focuses on a specific theme. The goal is getting people to think about the hardest questions in creation. Our retreats are also a great opportunity for students to get to know creationist researchers and scholars. So if you're in the southeastern U.S. or southern California, try out one of our retreats. You'll be very glad you did.

NOTES

1 There is an excellent modern English translation from Duke University Press: de Acosta, José. 2002. *Natural and Moral History of the Indies*. Translated by Frances López-Morillas. Durham, NC: Duke University Press.

2 Acosta 2002, p. 235.

3 There's another possibility that is popular in modern thought: The flood wasn't truly global, and it never actually killed the animals of the Americas. That did not seem to have occurred to Acosta though.

4 Acosta 2002, p. 236.

5 Acosta 2002, p. 62.

6 I've taken this discussion from a revised version of Barbour's book: Barbour, Ian G. 1997. *Religion and Science: Historical and Contemporary Issues*. San Francisco, CA: Harper San Francisco.

7 This quote is famously attributed to Anselm of Canterbury. See Williams, Thomas. 2016. "Saint Anselm." *The Stanford Encyclopedia of Philosophy*, edited by Edward N. Zalta. https://plato.stanford.edu/archives/spr2016/entries/anselm/.

8 No, I'm not kidding. Studies of modern human genomes and Neandertal DNA revealed that people of European or Asian

descent possess DNA inherited from Neandertal ancestors. I had a subset of my own genome sequenced by 23andMe, and they have a method of showing which parts of my genome are most likely inherited from my Neandertal forebears (http://23andme. com). For more information on the detection of Neandertal interbreeding, see Green, Richard E. and collaborators. 2010. "A Draft Sequence of the Neandertal Genome." *Science* 328: 710-722.

9   I read this poem online at The Literature Network, http://www. online-literature.com/tennyson/718/

10 Norton, John H., Malcolm A. Shepherd, Helen M. Long,, and William F. Kitt. 1992. "The Zooxanthellal Tubular System in the Giant Clam." *Biological Bulletin* 183: 503-506.

11 Berger, Lee R. and collaborators. 2010. "*Australopithecus sediba*: A New Species of *Homo*-like Australopith from South Africa." *Science* 328: 195-204.

12 Line, Peter. 2010. "*Australopithecus sediba*—No Human Ancestor." https://creation.com/sediba-not-human-ancestor. Thomas, Brian. 2010. "*Australopithecus sediba*: Another Human Ancestor?" http://www.icr.org/article/5344/.

13 The exact title was originally "Statistical Baraminology Analysis of Craniodental and Craniometric Data Identifies Genus *Homo* as the Human Holobaramin." I changed it to "Baraminological Analysis Places *Homo habilis*, *Homo rudolfensis*, and *Australopithecus sediba* in the Human Holobaramin." Read all about it in Wood, Todd Charles. 2010. "Baraminological Analysis Places *Homo habilis*, *Homo rudolfensis*, and *Australopithecus sediba* in the Human Holobaramin." *Answers Research Journal* 3: 71-90.

14 Strictly speaking, in an evolutionary sense the "missing link" isn't something anyone expects to find. If we evolved, we came from an entire population of ancestors, and the chances of actually finding a member of that population is vanishingly small. What we find instead are "stem taxa," branches of the evolutionary tree that grew from the base of the branch that led

to humanity. These creatures are distant cousins or siblings not strictly ancestors.

15 In case you're wondering, the evidence so far is pretty decisively in favor of Neandertals and *Homo erectus* being human and Lucy (*Australopithecus afarensis*) being a non-human ape. As I've mentioned, *Australopithecus sediba* is currently disputed (mostly by me). See Wood 2010.

16 That's carefully-chosen wording that is closer to the Hebrew language. "Flying things" includes more than what we biologists call "birds," and "swimming things" includes more than what we biologists call "fish."

17 Dawson, T.E. 1998. "Fog in the California Redwood Forest: Ecosystem Inputs and Use by Plants." *Oecologia* 117: 476-485.

18 Bree, C.R. 1860. *Species Not Transmutable, Nor the Result of Secondary Causes.* London: Groombridge and Sons, p. 254.

19 Bowler, Peter J. 1992. *The Eclipse of Darwinism.* Baltimore, MD: Johns Hopkins University Press.

20 Roberts, Jon H. 1988. *Darwinism and the Divine in America.* Notre Dame, IN: University of Notre Dame Press.

21 You can read Castelli's account, which I have summarized here, in his letter to Galileo translated into English in Drake, Stillman. 1957. *Discoveries and Opinions of Galileo.* New York: Anchor Books, pp. 151-152.

22 Read the original *Letter to the Grand Duchess Christina* in Drake 1957, pp. 175-216.

23 Drake 1957, p. 181.

24 Drake 1957, pp. 181-182.

25 Drake 1957, pp. 182-183.

26 I'm thinking especially of the work of Peter Enns and John Walton. Enns, Peter. 2012. *The Evolution of Adam.* Grand Rapids, MI: Baker Publishing Group. Walton, John H. 2009. *The Lost World of Genesis One.* Downers Grove, IL: Intervarsity Press.

27 For example, see Artigas, Mariano, Thomas F. Glick, and Rafael A. Martínez. 2006. *Negotiating Darwin: The Vatican Confronts Evolution 1877-1902.* Baltimore, MD: The Johns Hopkins University Press.

28 Sulston, J.E. and H.R. Horvitz. 1977. "Post-Embryonic Cell Lineages of the Nematode, *Caenorhabditis elegans.*" *Developmental Biology* 56: 110-156. Sulston, J.E., E. Schierenberg, J.G. White, and J.N. Thomson. 1983. "The Embryonic Cell Lineage of the Nematode *Caenorhabditis elegans.*" *Developmental Biology* 100: 64-119.

29 Kosinski R.A. and M. Zaremba. 2007. "Dynamics of the Model of the *Caenorhabditis elegans* Neural Network." *Acta Physica Polonica B* 38: 2201-2210.

30 The *C. elegans* Sequencing Consortium. 1998. "Genome Sequence of the Nematode *C. elegans*: A Platform for Investigating Biology." *Science* 282: 2012-2018.

31 See Wormbase for a sample of all of this data: http://www.wormbase.org

32 See for example, the pseudepigraphal I Enoch 7:2, "And when the angels, the sons of heaven, beheld them, they became enamoured of them, saying to each other, Come, let us select for ourselves wives from the progeny of men, and let us beget children." Alternatively, Augustine affirms that these "sons of God" were human and not angels in *City of God* XV.23.

33 I should mention that the theistic evolutionists that I've talked to really hate it when creationists say that. They are adamant that the Bible alone is enough to know that Genesis 1-11 is not historical. The textual "clues" they give in support of their contention are well-known questions that rarely caused a Christian scholar to accept a purely nonliteral reading of Genesis prior to the advent of modern science. Questions like "Where did Cain get his wife?" had a widely accepted answer (his sister) until scientific scoffers came along, and now those questions have been appropriated by evangelical critics of young-age creationism. These questions and curiosities did not convince the church fathers to radically

reinterpret scripture, and they do not convince me.

34 De Lubac, Henri. 1998. *Medieval Exegesis Volume 1: The Four Senses of Scripture*. Translated by Mark Sebanc. Grand Rapids, MI: William B. Eerdmans Publishing Company and Edinburgh: T&T Clark.

35 Origen. 1981. *Homilies on Genesis and Exodus*. Translated by Ronald E. Heine. Washington, DC: Catholic University of America Press, p. 75.

36 Rebecchi, Lorena, Tiziana Altiero, Roberto Guidetti, Michele Cesari, Roberto Bertolani, Manuela Negroni, and Angela M. Rizzo. 2009. "Tardigrade Resistance to Space Effects: First Results of Experiments on the LIFE-TARSE Mission on FOTON-M3 (September 2007)." *Astrobiology* 9(6): 581-591.

37 Brand, Leonard. 1979. "Field and Laboratory Studies on the Coconino Sandstone (Permian) Vertebrate Footprints and their Paleoecological Implications." *Palaeogeography, Palaeoclimatology, Palaeoecology* 28: 25-38.

38 Wood, T.C. 2016. "An Evaluation of *Homo naledi* and 'Early *Homo*' from a Young-Age Creationist Perspective." *Journal of Creation Theology and Science Series B: Life Sciences* 6: 14-30.

39 The Chimpanzee Sequencing and Analysis Consortium. 2005. "Initial Sequence of the Chimpanzee Genome and Comparison with the Human Genome." *Nature* 437: 69-87. Wood, T.C. 2006. "The Chimpanzee Genome and the Problem of Biological Similarity." *Occasional Papers of the BSG* 7: 1-18.

42 Kabadayi, Can and Mathias Osvath. 2017. "Ravens Parallel Great Apes in Flexible Planning for Tool-Use and Bartering." *Science* 357: 202-204.

41 Marzluff, John M., Jeff Walls, Heather N. Cornell, John C. Withey, and David P. Craig. 2010. "Lasting Recognition of Threatening People by Wild American Crows." *Animal Behaviour* 79: 699-707.

42 Morris, Herbert W. 1871. *Science and the Bible; or, the Mosaic Creation and Modern Discoveries*. Philadelphia: Ziegler &

McCurdy, p. 476.

43 For some interesting papers on the composition and interpretation of Genesis, see Mortenson, Terry and Thane H. Ury, editors. 2008. *Coming to Grips with Genesis*. Green Forest, AR: Master Books. Chou, Abner, editor. 2016. *What Happened in the Garden?* Grand Rapids, MI: Kregel Publications. VanDoodewaard, William. 2015. *The Quest for the Historical Adam*. Grand Rapids, MI: Reformation Heritage Books. Although I disagree with his conclusions, I also found Collins's book to be helpful in responding to some of the criticisms of theistic evolutionists. Collins, C. John. 2011. *Did Adam and Eve Really Exist?* Wheaton, IL: Crossway.

44 Collins, C. John. 1995. "The *Wayyiqtol* as 'Pluperfect': When and Why." *Tyndale Bulletin* 46(1): 117-140.

45 For example, see Enns 2012, who refers to this as the "Problem of the Pentateuch."

46 Turpin, Simon. 2013. "Did Death of Any Kind Exist Before the Fall? What the Bible Says About the Origin of Death and Suffering." *Answers Research Journal* 6: 99-116. Smith, Jr., Henry B. 2007. "Cosmic and Universal Death from Adam's Fall: an Exegesis of Romans 8:19-23a." *Journal of Creation* 21(1): 75-85.

47 Berndt, Chard. 2003. "The Pre-Fall Mortality of Aquatic Autotrophs and Other Designated Nephesh Kinds." *Creation Research Society Quarterly* 40: 85-89. Brand, Leonard. 2003. "What are the Limits of Death in Paradise?" *Journal of the Adventist Theological Society* 14(1): 74-85.

48 For example, see Berry, R.J. 1999. "This Cursed Earth: Is 'the Fall' Credible?" *Science and Christian Belief* 11: 29-49. Miller, Keith B. 2011. "'And God Saw That It Was Good': Death and Pain in the Created Order." *Perspectives on Science and the Christian Faith* 63(2): 85-94. Osborn, Ronald E. 2014. *Death before the Fall*. Downers Grove, IL: InterVarsity Press.

49 Thiel, Peter and Blake Masters. *Zero to One: Notes on Startups, or How to Build the Future*. New York: Crown Business, p. 96

50 Hartnett, John. 2007. *Starlight, Time, and the New Physics.* Eight Mile Plains, Australia: Creation Ministries International. Humphreys, D. Russell. 1994. *Starlight and Time.* Green Forest, AR: Master Books.

51 Lisle, Jason. 2010. "Anisotropic Synchrony Convention—A Solution to the Distant Starlight Problem." *Answers Research Journal* 3: 191-207.

52 DeYoung, Don B. "Mature Creation and Seeing Distant Starlight." *Journal of Creation* 24(3): 54-59.

53 For many examples of discordant radiometric dates, see Austin, Steven A. and Andrew A. Snelling. 1998. "Discordant Potassium-Argon Model and Isochron 'Ages' for Cardenas Basalt (Middle-Proterozoic) and Associated Diabase of Eastern Grand Canyon, AZ." In *Proceedings of the Fourth International Conference on Creationism,* edited by R.E. Walsh, pp. 35-51. Pittsburgh: Creation Science Fellowship. Snelling, Andrew A. 2003. "Whole-rock K-Ar Model and Isochron, and Rb-Sr, Sm-Nd and Pb-Pb Isochron, 'Dating' of the Somerset Dam Layered Mafic Intrusion, Australia." In *Proceedings of the Fifth International Conference on Creationism,* edited by R.L. Ivey, pp. 305-324. Pittsburgh: Creation Science Fellowship. Snelling, Andrew A., Steven A. Austin, and William A. Hoesch. 2003. "Radioisotopes in the Diabase Sill (Upper Precambrian) at Bass Rapids, Grand Canyon, Arizona: an Application and Test of the Isochron Dating Method." In *Proceedings of the Fifth International Conference on Creationism,* edited by R.L. Ivey, pp. 269-284. Pittsburgh: Creation Science Fellowship. Snelling, Andrew A. 2008. "Significance of Highly Discordant Radioisotope Dates for Precambrian Amphibolites in Grand Canyon, USA." In *Proceedings of the Sixth International Conference on Creationism,* edited by Andrew A. Snelling, pp. 407-424. Pittsburgh: Creation Science Fellowship.

54 For an early example of this consistency, see Kulp, J. Laurence. 1961. "Geologic Time Scale." *Science* 133:1105-1114.

55 Vardiman, Larry, Andrew A. Snelling, and Eugene F. Chaffin, editors. 2000. *Radioisotopes and the Age of the Earth: A Young-*

Earth Creationist Research Initiative. San Diego, CA: Institute for Creation Research and Chino Valley, AZ: Creation Research Society. Vardiman, Larry, Andrew A. Snelling, and Eugene F. Chaffin, editors. 2005. *Radioisotopes and the Age of the Earth: Results of a Young-Earth Creationist Research Initiative.* San Diego, CA: Institute for Creation Research and Chino Valley, AZ: Creation Research Society.

56 Vardiman, Snelling, and Chaffin 2000. Vardiman, Snelling, and Chaffin 2005.

57 See chapter 13 of Darwin, Charles. 1859. *On the Origin of Species by Means of Natural Selection.* London: John Murray.

58 For a fascinating introduction to the ancient DNA revolution, see Reich, David. 2018. *Who We Are and How We Got Here.* New York: Pantheon Books.

59 Green, Richard E. and collaborators. 2010. "A Draft Sequence of the Neandertal Genome." *Science* 328: 710-722. See also note 8.

60 Reich, David and collaborators. 2010. "Genetic History of an Archaic Hominin Group from Denisova Cave in Siberia." *Nature* 468: 1053-1060.

61 Wood, T.C. 2012. "Ancient mtDNA Implies a Nonconstant Molecular Clock in the Human Holobaramin." *Journal of Creation Theology and Science Series B: Life Sciences* 2: 18-26.

62 https://biologos.org/blogs/archive/a-survey-of-clergy-and-their-views-on-origins

63 For example, see Snelling, Andrew A. and David E. Rush. 1993. "Moon Dust and the Age of the Solar System." *Creation Ex Nihilo Technical Journal* 7(1): 2-42. Snelling, Andrew A. 1995. "The Whale Fossil in Diatomite, Lompoc, California." *Creation Ex Nihilo Technical Journal* 9(2): 244-258.

64 Sasaki, T., editor. 1978. *Collected Papers on the Carcass of an Unidentified Animal Trawled off New Zealand by the* Zuiyo-maru. Tokyo: La Société Franco-Japonaise d'Océanographie.

65 Wood, Todd Charles. 1997. "*Zuiyo-maru* Carcass Revisited: Plesiosaur or Basking Shark?" *Creation Research Society*

Quarterly 33: 292-295.

66 Wood, Todd Charles. 2013. "A Review of the Last Decade of Creation Biology Research on Natural History, 2003-2012." In *Proceedings of the Seventh International Conference on Creationism*, edited by Mark Horstemeyer. Pittsburgh: Creation Science Fellowship.

67 Austin, Steven A. 1986. "Mount St. Helens and Catastrophism." In *Proceedings of the First International Conference on Creationism*, edited by R.S. Crowell, pp. 3-9. Pittsburgh: Creation Science Fellowship. Austin, Steven A., editor. *Grand Canyon: Monument to Catastrophe.* Santee, CA: Institute for Creation Research. Coffin, Harold G. 1997. "The Yellowstone Petrified 'Forests.'" *Origins* 24(1): 2-44.

68 For more information on this extraordinary dinosaur excavation, see http://dinosaurproject.swau.edu/.

69 Berger, Lee R. and collaborators. 2015. "*Homo naledi*, a new species of the genus *Homo* from the Dinaledi Chamber, South Africa." *eLife* 4: e09560.

INDEX

To learn more about the quest, visit Core Academy of Science online at **http://coresci.org** or check out Todd's Blog at **http://toddcwood.blogspot.com**.